A Synthetic Approach To Lip Reading

MATERIALS FOR THE CHILD OF GRADE SCHOOL AGE

by

GEORGE S. HASPIEL, Ph.D.

Assistant Director
Speech and Hearing Clinic
The Pennsylvania State University

EXPRESSION COMPANY

Magnolia   Massachusetts

To my wife, Marlene,
and to my children,
Erica, Adam and Lisa,
whose encouragement and
confidence made this
work possible.

PREFACE

The use of visual cues probably is the oldest and most readily available method used by the hearing handicapped who are sighted to understand the communication of others. Only cupping of the hand behind the ear ranks close to vision as a natural aid to hearing.

Although manual signs, finger spelling and other formalized schemes using non-speech movements generally are dependent upon vision, they are qualitatively different from speech reading (lip reading) for they require special skill and knowledge on the part of the person attempting to communicate with the hearing impaired individual. In contrast, speech reading by the hearing handicapped requires only that the speaker use a language familiar to the hearing impaired member of the conversation.

Here is not the place to enter the controversy regarding whether the deaf should be taught by the oral method, the manual method, or by a combination of methods. Suffice it to say that speech reading is recognized as a useful skill, it is beneficial to the hard-of-hearing as well as to the deaf, it should be taught to children with hearing impairments, and procedures for its teaching are a continuing need.

In this manual is presented a series of lessons in speech reading for the elementary school age child. They are useful to the trained therapist as well as to the parent who may be undertaking home training of the child. The lessons are not designed specifically for the child who is deaf, although they may be so used. Rather, they assume that the child has basic language and speech and enough hearing ability to be classified as hard-of-hearing. The activities are graded in speech reading difficulty, are designed to be attractive to children, are useful for group training, and not only give the therapist direct and specific teaching materials but they also are suggestive of additional procedures and materials which may be developed. As such, this manual becomes a very useful and up-to-date addition to the materials available to the hearing rehabilitation of acoustically handicapped children.

BRUCE M. SIEGENTHALER

State College, Pennsylvania

CONTENTS

INTERMEDIATE LESSONS

FOREWORD

The material in this book was prepared for the lip reading instruction of children of grade school age, the group that perhaps requires our attention and concerted efforts in communication therapy more than any other portion of the hearing-impaired population.

The vocabulary, language complexity, language development sequence and interest level of the material were all carefully considered in putting together a graded series of lessons designed for young children. Most of the lip reading material available today, while applicable with the adult, cannot be readily adapted for the child. A collection of specially prepared units for the five to fourteen year age group has long been needed.

The primary concern in the design of these lessons was the development of synthetic lip readers* and consequently, there is no sound movement drill or single word drill nor is attention called to the specific movement of the oral musculature in production. Rather, the child becomes familiar with language concepts and construction through unified lessons around a central theme.

My gratitude is offered to the following

people for invaluable assistance given in the preparation of this book; my former students at the State University of New York at Geneseo who originated some of the materials used; the staff and students in Speech and Hearing at Pennsylvania State University whose advice was of great help in the organization of the book; Dr. Eugene McDonald, Director of the Speech and Hearing Clinic and Dr. Bruce Siegenthaler, Associate Professor at Penn State for the help given in formulating some of the basic concepts stated herein; the out-patient children at State University of New York; and the children in the summer program at Pennsylvania State University with whom much of the material was employed at various times; and to my family, Marlene, Erica and Adam who have encouraged the production of this book in so many ways.

---

*Definition of synthetic lip reading: the understanding of spoken language by perception of the complete communication situation which includes facial and body clues plus additional clues arising from all other components of the situation. This is in contrast to analytic lip reading which may be defined as the reconstruction of spoken language using the phonemes which have been identified by the lip reader.

INTRODUCTION

A DEFINITION OF LIP READING

The term, lip reading, is a traditional one which has been employed by hearing therapists to describe one dimension of therapy designed to minimize communication problems arising from a hearing loss. It is not an operational term since we realize that much more than identifying visible phonemes is involved in successfully understanding spoken language.

Lip reading will be used in this book to indicate therapy in which the child learns to use facial and body clues plus additional clues which arise from the other components of the complete communication situation.

Since much of what is said is not visible, skill in lip reading cannot be acquired by simply learning to read the movements of the tongue and lips; since many sounds and words in our language are homophonous, it would be useless to merely develop adeptness in combining visible and invisible components; and since the eye functions less rapidly than the ear in the analysis of spoken sounds, it would be impossible to replace the sensory channel of audition with that of vision by attempting to train the eye to undertake the analytic role of the ear. Therefore, to prepare the child for understanding spoken language, it is necessary to train him in some fashion other than an analytic approach.

The child must be trained to synthesize the known and the unknown rapidly without laboring over the miniscule portions of what he can analyze. This may be accomplished by (1) giving him a great deal of practice in lip reading *complete* language units which become progressively longer and more complex and (2) placing him in life situations which permit the utilization of situational clues. Unfortunately, the latter can seldom be accomplished in most therapy programs because of time and physical plant considerations. The attempt has been made to recreate the natural environment for specific language in these lessons but obviously this is artificial. The most successful application of this material will be made by combining the lessons with a home study program administered by the parents.

THE USE OF VOICE

In training the child to lip read, as in training him in any sensory or motor performance area, one basic principle should be remembered: maximum potential is realized by overtraining. This concept may be extended by stating that optimal performance under less rigorous circumstances is achieved by overtraining under more difficult conditions. An example of this is furnished us by the track athlete who races the mile with lead weights in his shoes so that he may more effectively run the half-mile with ordinary track shoes.

In applying this principle to lip reading therapy, the lessons are presented without voice to increase the child's reliance on vision and to develop maximally his skill in using visual clues. When given the opportunity to combine visual and auditory clues, as he is given in the final lessons of each section, the child does so more easily and efficiently than would be the case if over learning had not been accomplished.

Since the parent cannot be expected to achieve skill in voiceless oral production, the home study section of the book may be given with soft voice.

AUDITORY TRAINING AND LIP READING

Auditory training may be described as therapy which develops the residual hearing to its maximum potential. Three goals of auditory training: 1) most effective possible use of the hearing aid in picking up sounds used for language and non-language purposes; 2) maximum use of auditory clues for the recognition and discrimination of environmental sounds; 3) maximum use of auditory clues for the understanding of spoken language.

The development of residual hearing requires

a methodical, step by step approach in which the child first becomes aware of sound, then learns to recognize and discriminate between sounds, and finally is able to use speech sounds to understand spoken language. The achieving of this end goal is not accomplished by simply putting a hearing aid on the child and allowing him to sit in a sound-environment.

Auditory training is particularly important for the young child since he has had such relatively limited experience in listening. Much of his success in acquiring adequate communication ability will be due to the skill with which the therapist guides him through many listening experiences and to the *number* of listening experiences. Auditory training is much too important to squeeze into a few minutes of the lip reading lesson, and the hours in lip reading therapy much too important to shorten. The only solution seems to be separate but concomitant programs of auditory training and lip reading. The skills developed dichotomously in these separate practice periods will be welded in the final lip reading lessons in which the child listens to speech while lip reading.

ANALYSIS OF THE LESSONS

OBJECTIVES

These lessons have the following objectives: 1) developing familiarity with everyday language and vocabulary; 2) increasing the child's ability to lip read increasingly more difficult language concepts; 3) inducing and maintaining a high level of interest in lip reading by the use of motivating materials.

INTRA-LESSON SEQUENCE
FOR PRIMARY LESSONS

The Primary lesson is divided into three sections and follows the order of the objectives given above. It is obvious, however, that there must be a great deal of overlapping in the construction of a given lesson. Most of the new vocabulary for the lesson is introduced in Activity I and is presented in simple sentence structure. Activity II usually develops this vocabulary in a situational schema employing more complex language than Activity I and adds related vocabulary. Activity III is a game period during which the children take active physical and/or verbal part and is constructed around the theme and vocabulary introduced in the first activity.

INTRA-LESSON SEQUENCE
FOR INTERMEDIATE LESSONS

Again, as in the Primary lessons, the objectives are developed primarily in the separate activities. Activities I, II, and IV are comparable to Activities I, II, and III of the Primary section lesson. But now a new unit, the *fable,* is introduced. The fable, Activity III in the Intermediate lesson, is unrelated to the central theme of the other activities within a lesson. This is so for two reasons: first, the fable lends needed variety to the Intermediate lesson which is considerably longer and contains more fatiguing, complex material; secondly, it allows the teacher an opportunity to introduce and explain important concepts using increasingly more difficult language.

INTER-LESSON SEQUENCE
OF LESSONS

This material has been prepared and arranged so that the vocabulary and language used in each succeeding lesson are based on the vocabulary and language of previous lessons and are graduated in difficulty. It is therefore important that the order of lessons from the first Primary to the final Intermediate lesson be maintained. Additional lessons can be inserted by using the topics in the Appendix (B) employing the language and vocabulary of the immediately preceeding lessons.

HOW TO GIVE THE LESSON

GENERAL DIRECTIONS TO THE TEACHER

1. The class is arranged so that all children may see the teacher's face equally well.
2. The teacher is seated so that her face is evenly lighted to prevent shadows from being formed.

3. The children are seated so that they face a neutral, non-fatiguing, non-distracting background for the teacher's face and body.

4. When the children become proficient in lip reading the teacher's face from a front view, she first changes position so that they may have a three-quarter view and then later changes to a profile position. In the Intermediate section, the fables may be given while the teacher walks slowly before the group thereby changing positions frequently.

5. No voice is used until Lesson Twenty of the Primary section and Lesson Seventeen of the Intermediate. Rather, a completely normal appearing oral production is employed without use of either voice or whisper. While this is not simple to do the first time attempted, it is not difficult to accomplish before long with sufficient mirror practice. These lessons should not be attempted until the skill of silent production is mastered.

SPECIFIC INSTRUCTIONS
FOR GIVING THE LESSON

1. Sentences:

Unless otherwise indicated in the *procedure* of an activity, employ the following sequence in the presentation of a sentence:

    a. Read the sentence through once.

    b. If it is not understood from the first reading, repeat the sentence as it is.

     c. If necessary, re-phrase it but retain the cue word.
     d. Give the sentence without voice except for the cue word which is said aloud.
     e. Give the entire sentence aloud.

2. Cue words:

The cue words designated in all these activities are either new vocabulary, proper names, or contain invisible phonemes which make the word difficult to read. The cue words should be given first with voice, then without voice and their meanings completely explained. Use any pictures or figures employed in the various activities to help clarify the cue words.

3. Fables:

The fables are given first by going through each sentence with the entire group (see *Sentences* above); the children repeat the sentence each time. The fable is given in its entirety without interruption once the sentences have been repeated correctly by the class. The questions following the fables are asked of individuals rather than the class as a whole.

HOME STUDY PROGRAM

Before initiating therapy, the parents of the children are asked to participate in a group conference at which time the program content and goals will be explained.

The parents must be impressed with the importance of situational clues which arise from a given language circumstance and told that they may play a role which is equally important as that of the therapist by giving their children numerous opportunities to utilize such situational clues.

The parents are to be instructed in the following principles of therapy.

THE USE OF VOICE

Although the lessons given in the formal program of lip reading are presented without voice, the parents may use a soft voice which will furnish some but not all auditory clues.

MANNER OF ARTICULATION

The parents are instructed to use a normal delivery. They are not to attempt to speak any more perfectly or clearly than they would usually.

POSITION OF THE PARENT

At first, a seated position of both the child and parent should be employed. Explain that a front view of the face is more easily lip read and that such a view should be used until the child becomes proficient. Then, the parent is told to change to a three-quarter position and finally to a profile view. When the parent feels the child can lip read easily under these circumstances, she may change to a standing position and move around slowly to increase the challenge.

LIGHTING AND BACKGROUND

Even lighting which casts no shadows on the speaker's face should be used whenever possible. However, there will be many environmental conditions in which this will be difficult or impossible to realize. When this is the case, the parent is told that the normal situation is of primary importance and the lighting secondary.

A background which is not fatiguing to the eyes such as bright sun light or glaring colors is desirable but again, as with lighting, this is to be considered less important than the normal environment.

LENGTH OF THE LESSON

The first few times the parents meet with their children should be short, no longer than ten minutes. As they become more confident and as the children begin to enjoy the home lessons, increase this to fifteen, then twenty minutes. No more than a half-hour lesson is to be given with the Primary children. The Intermediate children can spend as much time as *they* wish but at no time force any of the children, Primary or Intermediate, to stay in the lip reading situation when it becomes uncomfortable to do so.

LESSON TOPICS

A copy of the table of contents should be

mimeographed for each parent and the suggestion made that they try to follow these themes in a real life situation when it is possible. Since much of the vocabulary which is used in the formal lesson will be duplicated in the life situation, it would be advantageous if the parents were to give the home lesson soon after the formal lesson. This will reinforce the vocabulary and language already introduced.

PRIMARY
LESSONS

LESSON ONE

ACTIVITY I PARTS OF THE BODY

Material: Blackboard and chalk. Cue words:
man, head, hair, eyes, nose, mouth, ears, neck,
shoulders, arms, body, legs, feet, toes.

Procedure: The children are called on individually to lip read sentences containing parts of
the body. As they repeat the sentences correctly,
add the parts of the body mentioned to a circle
sketch of a man on the board.

Sentences: I will draw a man's ....

Complete the carrier phrase with the parts of
the body.

ACTIVITY II

PUTTING CLOTHES ON THE MAN

Material: Blackboard sketch on the board
from the previous activity. New cue words:
hat, collar, coat, pants, socks, shoes, tie, buttons,
pockets, gloves.

Procedure: The children are called on individually to lip read the directions below and having done so add to the figure the articles of
clothing mentioned.

Sentences: Complete the carrier phrase with
the body parts and clothing pairs.

Put a .... on the man's ....

hat	head
collar	neck
coat	body
pants	legs
socks	feet
shoes	socks
tie	shirt
buttons	shirt
pockets	coat
gloves	hands

ACTIVITY III COMMANDS

Material: Blackboard and chalk. Cue words: touch, put, place, left, right.

Procedure: The children are placed in an even row facing the blackboard so that they may see the cue words of the previous activities. They are to perform the activities given in the sentences as soon as they know them.

Sentences:

Touch your toes.
Touch your head.
Touch your mouth.
Touch your feet.
Touch your eyes.

Put your hand on your hair.
Put your hand on your foot.
Put your hand on your neck.
Put your hand on your shoulder.
Put your hand on your ear.

Place your *left* hand on your shirt.
Place your *right* hand on your pants.
Place your left hand on your shoes.
Place your right hand on your socks.
Place your right hand on your buttons.

LESSON TWO

ACTIVITY I

WHAT DO WE SEE AT THE CIRCUS?

Material: Flannel board and felt figures of the following objects: circus tent, flag, clown, boy, girl, bear, lion, monkey, large ball. These figures are used for explaining the cue words.

Procedure: The children are to build a circus scene, using the felt figures which are placed on a table before them. They are called on individually to repeat the sentence and to place the object(s) on the board as directed in the sentence.

Sentences:

Place the circus tent on the board.
Put the flag at the top of the tent.
Put the clown under the tent.
The boy is looking at the tent.
The girl is looking at the clown.
A bear is under the tent.
A lion is by the bear.
The monkey is playing with a big ball.

ACTIVITY II   A DAY AT THE CIRCUS

Material: Flannel board and figures from Activity I. The new cue words are: Betty, Bobby Jones, holding, threw, caught, bounced, air, landed, home.

Procedure: The children are called on individually to repeat the sentences and to then place the figures correctly as the story progresses.

Sentences:

Betty and Bobby Jones went to the circus.
They saw the circus tent.
They saw a clown in a big hat.
The clown was holding a ball.
He threw the ball to the bear.
The bear caught the ball on his nose.
The bear bounced the ball to the monkey.
The monkey threw the ball in the air.
The ball landed on the lion's head.
Then, Betty and Bobby went home.

ACTIVITY III   ANIMAL CATCH

Material: Name plates with neck cords for the following: Mr. Bear, Mr. Lion, Mr. Monkey, Mr. Elephant, Mr. Clown. A brightly colored beach ball is also used.

Procedure: The children form a semi-circle around the teacher who directs each where to throw the ball. If a child throws the ball to the wrong person, he is eliminated from the game. Continue until only one person is left; this child then gives the directions to the others.

Sentences: Throw the ball to Mr. } Bear
Elephant
Clown
Monkey
Lion

LESSON THREE

ACTIVITY I NAME THE ANIMAL

Material: Flannel board and the following felt figures: pig, cow, duck, chicken, sheep, rooster, horse. Use the figures for explaining the animal names.

Procedure: Give the sentences to the children as a group and instruct them to say the animal's name aloud as soon as they think they know it. Inform the class that you will keep score and that the child with the most correct answers will be the "teacher" for a game at the close of the period.

Sentences:

This animal has four legs.
He has a curly tail.
His nose is flat.
What is his name?

Answer: pig.

This animal has four legs.
He has a long tail.
He gives us milk.
What is his name?

Answer: cow.

This bird lives on a farm.
He likes to swim in the water.
He has webbed feet.
What is his name?

Answer: duck.

This bird lives on a farm.
She lays eggs for the farmer.
Sometimes we eat her for dinner.
What is her name?

Answer: chicken.

This animal lives on a farm.
He has wool on his back.
We makes clothes from his wool.
What is his name?

Answer: sheep.

This bird lives on a farm.
He wakes us in the morning.
He is not very good to eat.
What is his name?

Answer: rooster.

This animal has four legs.
He runs very fast.
He can carry us on his back.
What is his name?

Answer: horse.

ACTIVITY II THE BARNYARD

Material: Flannel board and figures used in the previous activity. Cue words: barnyard, hen, in, by, on, next to, near, by himself.

Procedure: The children are called on individually to follow the directions given in the sentences.

Sentences:

Put the hen in the barnyard.
Place the duck next to the hen.
The pig is all by himself.
The rooster is on the pig's back.
The horse is by himself.
The cow is near the horse.
The sheep is by the pig.

ACTIVITY III HOP, SKIP, AND JUMP

Material: Flannel board and felt figures from the previous activities. Cue words: the names of the children in the class; hop, skip, jump.

Procedure: Call the child who had the most correct answers in Activity I to the front of the class and have him go through the children's names and cue words. Then, line up the children across the room from the flannel board and tell them they will be given individual instructions by their classmate to either hop, skip or jump (broad jump) to a particular animal and to touch it. As each performs the correct activity and touches the animal called for, he becomes the "teacher" and may call upon another child.

Sentences: (Child's name), $\left.\begin{array}{l} \text{hop} \\ \text{skip} \\ \text{jump} \end{array}\right\}$ to the..........

LESSON FOUR

ACTIVITY I   DIFFERENT TIMES OF DAY

Material: Blackboard, chalk.   See *procedures* for the cue words.

Procedure: Write the following words on the board in two columns: Column one: dinner time, breakfast time, lunch time, bedtime, daytime, night time. Column two: sandwiches, potatoes, cereal, prayers, moon, sun. When the children answer the questions correctly, they go to the board and draw a line between the words named in columns one and two.

Sentences:

Would you eat sandwiches at bedtime or lunchtime?

Would you eat potatoes at lunchtime or dinner time?

Would you eat cereal at dinnertime or breakfast time?

Would you say your prayers at bedtime or in the daytime?

Would the sun shine in the daytime or in the night time?

Would the moon come out in the daytime or in the night time?

ACTIVITY II WHAT TIME IS IT?

Material: Large cardboard clock with movable hands. The following cue words are given: all the hours of the day, morning, evening, afternoon, supper, school, home, sleep, television, lunch, class.

Procedure: Read the sentences to the children individually and have them change the hands of the clock to the time named.

Sentences:

Right now the time is .... o'clock.
In one hour, the time will be .... o'clock.
We get up at seven o'clock in the morning.
We eat supper at six o'clock in the evening.
School starts at nine o'clock in the morning.
We go home at four o'clock in the afternoon.
We go to sleep at eight o'clock in the evening.
What do you see on television at five o'clock?
We eat lunch at twelve o'clock.
What class are you in at two o'clock?

ACTIVITY III COMMANDS

See Lesson One for material and procedure.

LESSON FIVE

ACTIVITY I I SEE A TREE

Material: Blackboard, chalk. Cue words: brown, red, green, yellow, orange, blue, fruit.

Procedure: Have the children draw a tree, one line at a time, by connecting any two numbers designated by the teacher. Each segment is added by the child after he repeats a sentence correctly. Continue the drawing until someone guesses the name of the object. The drawing is made on a blackboard chart made up of five columns of numbers from one through fifty; the first column contains the numbers one through ten, the second column is made of the numbers eleven through twenty, and so on.

Sentences:

This can be small or big.
It has a brown body.
It has big, strong feet.
It has beautiful green hair.
Sometimes its hair turns red.
Sometimes it wears yellow flowers.
Sometimes it wears orange fruit.
Blue birds and red birds sit in it.
Green grass grows between its toes.

ACTIVITY II A Spring Story

Material: Flannel board and the following figures: blue sky, fluffy cloud, green lawn, tall tree, green leaves, yellow daffodils, purple violets. Use these figures for cue words.

Procedure: As the children repeat the sentences, they take the item named and place it on the flannel board.

Sentences:

In Spring we see a blue sky.

There are fluffy clouds in the blue sky in Spring.

There is a green lawn under the fluffy cloud in the blue sky in Spring.

There is a tall tree on the green lawn under the fluffy cloud in the blue sky in Spring.

There are green leaves in the tall tree on the green lawn under the fluffy cloud in the blue sky in Spring.

There are yellow daffodils and purple violets under the green leaves in the tall tree on the green lawn under the fluffy cloud in the blue sky in Spring.

ACTIVITY III Lip Reading Bingo

Materials: Bingo game.

Procedure: This is played as one usually plays bingo but no voice is used.

LESSON SIX

ACTIVITY I DRESSING THE JONES FAMILY

Material: Blackboard, chalk. Cue words: hat, shirt, coat, tie, belt, pants, socks, shoes, buttons, blouse, skirt, dress, purse, blanket, collar, leash.

Procedure: Draw circle figures of a man, woman, boy, girl, and small dog, introducing them to the class as the Jones family whom they will meet many times in the future. The child who repeats the statement draws the article named on the appropriate figure.

Sentences: Father Jones
Mother Jones
Bobby Jones } is wearing a ....
Betty Jones
Sparky

ACTIVITY II

THE JONES FAMILY GOES SHOPPING

Material: Blackboard, chalk. Cue words: downtown, wanted, clothes, needed, school.

Procedure: Draw circle figures of Betty and Bobby Jones. The children are to draw colored clothes on the figures in response to the sentences.

Sentences:

The Jones family went downtown.

Betty and Bobby wanted new clothes for school.

Bobby wanted a blue hat.
Betty needed a red dress.
Bobby wanted a white shirt.
He needed a yellow and green tie.
Betty needed a skirt and blouse.
She wanted a purple blouse and a red skirt.
Bobby wanted orange shoes.
Betty needed white socks.
Betty wanted a brown purse.

ACTIVITY III COMMANDS

Material: None.

Procedure: See Lesson One, Activity III. Sentences: Use the carrier phrases below with the articles of clothing in Activity I of this lesson.

Put your hand on your ....
Put your finger on your ....
Touch your finger to your ....

LESSON SEVEN

ACTIVITY I WHAT SEASON IS IT?

Material: Large slot chart and four name cards with the names of the seasons: Summer, Spring, Winter, Fall. Pictures of the following objects and scenes: snowman, ice skating, picnic, raking leaves, burning leaves, planting seeds,

swimming, going back to school, taking a vacation, Santa Claus, kite, playing marbles, fishing,
birds flying. Use these pictures for cue words.

Procedure: The children are called upon individually to repeat the sentence, and having
done so are allowed to place the pictures under
the appropriate name card.

Sentences:

We can build a snowman in the Winter.
We can rake leaves in the Fall.
We can go back to school in the Fall.
We can see Santa Claus in the Winter.
We can take a vacation in the Spring.
We can go fishing in the Summer.
We can burn leaves in the Fall.
We can go ice skating in the Winter.
We can play marbles in the Summer.
We can fly a kite in the Fall.
We can go on a picnic in the Spring.
We can see the birds again in the Spring.

ACTIVITY II

SPARKY LOSES THE SNOW BOY

Material: Blackboard, chalk. Cue words:
snowed, fluffy, puppy, play, snowman, hurt,
afraid, all day, after a while, sleep, the next day,
friend, warm, sunny, son, snowboy, puddle.

Procedure: Read the story to the class, having
them repeat each sentence after you. When the
story is finished, ask the questions given below.

Sentences:

One day, in the middle of winter, it snowed.
There was white, fluffy snow all over.

Sparky, a little brown puppy, came out to play.

He saw some boys building a snowman.

At first, Sparky was afraid of the big snowman.

But the snowman did not hurt him.

Sparky played with the snowman all day.

After a while, Sparky had to go home to sleep.
The next day was warm and sunny.

When Sparky ran out to play, the snowman had gone away.

But he had left a little snow boy for Sparky.

Sparky played with the snow boy until it was time for lunch.

Sparky come back to play after lunch but the snow boy was gone.

All that Sparky could find was a puddle of water.

Questions:

Why was Sparky afraid of the snowman?
Why did he stop playing with the snowman?
What was the weather like the next day?
Who was waiting to play with Sparky?
When did Sparky stop playing with the snow boy?
What do you think happened to the snow boy?
Where do you think the snowman went?

ACTIVITY III DARTS

Material: A set of suction tip darts, pictures used in Activity I.

Procedure: Scotch tape the pictures to the blackboard. Have the children throw the darts at the pictures using the carrier phrase, *"Janey, throw the dart at the ...."* The child reaching a goal of five, with each hit worth one, becomes the "teacher" and calls the orders to the class.

LESSON EIGHT

ACTIVITY I WHERE DO I GROW?

Material: Flannel board, felt figures. Cue words: carrot, apple, grapes, cabbage, vine, seed, potato, orange, watermelon, corn, ground (thin strip of brown felt).

Procedure: When the children answer the questions, they take from the table the figures mentioned and place them on the flannel board.

Sentences:

I am a carrot. Where do I grow?
I am an apple. Where do I grow?
I am a bunch of grapes. Where do I grow?
I am a head of cabbage. Where do I grow?
I am a thin, green vine. Where do I grow?
I am a tiny apple seed. Where do I grow?
I am a big brown potato. Where do I grow?
I am a round orange. Where do I grow?

I am a big, green watermelon. Where do 1 grow?

I am tall, yellow corn. Where do I grow?

(Answers to all the questions: above the ground or below the ground).

ACTIVITY II THE GROCERY STORE

Material: Flannel board, felt figures. Cue words: Mother Jones, Betty Jones, Bobby Jones, shopping cart, car, peas, coffee, tomatoes, eggs, bacon, hot dogs, man, cheese, milk, bags, money, super market. Additional cue words: dairy, canned, meat.

Procedure: The children are given sentences to act out with the felt figures mentioned in the sentences.

Sentences:

Mother took Betty and Bobby to the store.
They went in mother's car.
When they got there, Bobby got a cart.
Mother told them what to get.
She got the meat.
Bobby got the canned foods.
Betty got the dairy food.
Betty put some eggs into the shopping cart.
Bobby put some peas into the shopping cart.
Mother put a ham into the shopping cart.
Betty put some cheese into the shopping cart.
Bobby put some coffee into the shopping cart.

Mother put some bacon into the shopping cart.

Betty put some milk into the shopping cart.

Bobby put some tomatoes into the shopping cart.

Mother put some hot dogs into the shopping cart.

ACTIVITY III   I WENT TO THE STORE

Material: None.

Procedure: The children are seated in a semi-circle, and are instructed to watch each other's lips closely. One child starts the game by saying the carrier phrase, completing it with the name of some food. The second child repeats the entire sentence and adds another food item. This continues until someone misses or forgets one of the words. This child is eliminated and the game continues. The winner is the last remaining child.

Sentences:

I went to the store and bought some ....

LESSON NINE

ACTIVITY I   HANGING UP THE CLOTHES

Material: Flannel board and the following felt figures: clothes line, pajamas, mittens, dresses, socks, diapers, blue jeans, apron, handkerchief, shoes, tie. The following cue words are given: clothes, hang, wear, under, babies, play, wash, cold, over, around.

Procedure: The sentences are given to the whole class which is instructed to shout out the name of the clothes as soon as they know it. The child who answers first is given the article to place on the board. The one with the greatest number of first correct answers will be the "call-er" for Bingo at the end of the hour.

Sentences:

Hang this up so we can put clothes on it.
We wear these when we go to bed.
We wear these on our hands.
Girls wear these but boys do not.
We wear these under our shoes.
We wear these over our socks.
Babies wear these all of the time.
Boys wear these when they play.
Mother wears this when she washes the dishes.
We use this when we have a cold.
A boy wears this with a suit.

ACTIVITY II

MOTHER AND BETTY DO THE WASH

Material: Blackboard, chalk. Cue words: soap suds, bleach, sheets, hamper, downstairs, washing machine, light clothes, pillow slips, underwear, dark clothes, play clothes.

Procedure: The class repeats the sentences together, but the questions following the story are answered individually.

Sentences:

Mother and Betty are getting ready to do the wash.

Mother gets the soap suds and the bleach.

Betty takes the sheets off of the beds.

Mother takes the hamper downstairs.

They are ready to start the wash.

Betty puts the soap suds and bleach into the washing machine.

Mother puts some clothes into the machine.

First, Mother puts in the light clothes.

This would be the sheets, pillowslips and the underwear.

Then, she puts in the dark clothes.

This would be the socks, pants and play clothes.

Questions:

What were the first things Mother and Betty needed?

What did Betty get from the bedroom to be washed?

What clothes did Mother put in first?

What clothes did Mother put in next?

Why do you think she didn't put them together?

Why do you think she put the lights clothes in first?

ACTIVITY III BINGO

For materials and procedure see Lesson Five, Activity III. The "caller" will be the winner of Activity I of this lesson.

LESSON TEN

ACTIVITY I SPORT RIDDLES

Material: Blackboard, chalk. Cue words: paddle, ball, ping-pong, people, person, club, hole, eighteen, bat, baseball, yourself, swimming, ice, ice skating.

Procedure: Each child is given one complete riddle to solve. Repeat and re-phrase as much as necessary but do not continue the activity until the riddle is answered.

Sentences:

Two people or four people can play this game.
They use paddles and a ball.
The ball is very small.
They play the game on a table.

Answer: Ping pong

One, two, three or four people play this game.
They use a small, hard ball.
They hit the ball with a long club.
They hit the ball into a small hole.

Answer: Golf

Eighteen people play this game.
They use a hard, white ball.
One team hits the ball with a bat.
The other team tries to catch the ball.

Answer: Baseball

This can be done by one person.
No bat or ball is used.
This is done in the water.
You wear a special suit.

Answer: Swimming

This can be done by one person.
Special shoes must be worn.
It is done in winter.
It is done on the ice.

Answer: Ice Skating

ACTIVITY II

Bobby Jones Learns Not to Brag

Material: Blackboard, chalk. Cue words: sports, baseball, football, ping pong, ride, ice skate, swim, decided, pond, Sparky, practiced, wagged, brag.

Procedure: The children repeat the sentences and answer the questions individually.

Sentences:

Bobby was very good at sports.
He could play baseball and football.

He could play ping pong and ride a horse.
He could even ice skate very well.
But Bobby could not swim.
One day, he decided to learn how to swim.
He took Sparky, his dog, and went swimming.
He went to a pond outside of town.
He practiced very hard.
Finally, he learned to swim.
He could swim about five feet.
He said to Sparky, "See how good I am."
Sparky wagged his tail.
Sparky was so happy that he jumped into the water.
He swam all the way to the other side.
Bobby did not brag any more.

Questions:

What sports was Bobby good in playing?
What sport was Bobby poor in doing?
Why did he take a dog instead of a boy when he went swimming?
How far could Bobby swim?
Was Sparky happy that Bobby could swim?
Why didn't Bobby brag any more?

ACTIVITY III FISHING GAME

Material: Horseshoe magnet attached to a string, pictures of the cue words with paper clips attached. Cue words: ping pong, skating, swimming, baseball, football, hockey, golf, riding.

Procedure: Each child with the magnet takes his turn fishing for a picture. He then describes the picture to the class which tries to guess the activity. The child who guesses the sport keeps the picture.

LESSON ELEVEN

ACTIVITY I Who Am I?

Material: Blackboard, chalk, animal and bird pictures. Cue words: pony, cat, bear, skunk, cow, monkey, butterfly, turtle, worm, mouse. Additional cue words: like, look, live, land, stable, circus, house, woods, honey, stripe, jungle.

Procedure: Each child is given a riddle to solve which is repeated and re-phrased as much as necessary. Do not continue the activity until the riddle is solved.

Sentences:

I live in a stable.
I look like a horse but am smaller.
Children like to ride me at the circus.

Answer: pony

I live in a house.
I have a long tail.
I do not like dogs or mice.

Answer: cat

I live in the woods.
I am very strong.
I like to eat honey.

Answer: bear

I live in the woods.
I have black fur with a white stripe.
Sometimes I smell very bad.

Answer: skunk

I live on a farm.
I eat grass and hay.
I give white milk to you.

Answer: cow

I live in the jungle.
I climb tall trees.
I like to eat bananas.

Answer: monkey

I fly in the air.
I am not a bird.
I was once a caterpillar.

Answer: butterfly

I live in the water.
I can live on land, too.
I have a hard shell on my back.

Answer: turtle

I live in the ground.
I have no arms or feet.
Boys take me fishing with them.

Answer: worm

I live in a house.
I like to eat cheese.
I don't like cats very much.

Answer: mouse

ACTIVITY II   A TRIP TO THE ZOO

Material: Blackboard, chalk. Cue words:
work, family, park, parked, animal, ground,
chasing, late.

Procedure: The story is told to the class as a
whole which repeats each sentence together. The
questions are answered individually.

Sentences:

Father Jones came home early from work
one day.

He wanted to take the family for a trip to
the Zoo.

Mother, Betty, Bobby and Father got into the
car.

They drove to the park and parked the car.

They started to walk to the animal houses.

Bobby stopped suddenly.

He sat on the ground to watch a worm.

Betty made everyone stop next.

She wanted to watch a butterfly.

They started to walk again, but Mother and Father stopped.

They wanted to watch a cat chasing a mouse.

By this time it was very late.

Bobby said, "We'd better hurry. We won't see any animals today. We keep stopping to look at animals."

Questions:

Why did Father come home early?

What did they do with the car at the park?

Why did Bobby stop?

Why did Betty stop?

Why did Mother and Father Jones stop?

ACTIVITY III

I'M THINKING OF AN ANIMAL

Material: None. Animal names from Activity I and II are on the board.

Procedure: The children line up against a wall and a goal line is drawn about six feet from them. They shout out the name of the animal given in the sentences as soon as they recognize it. If they have the correct name, they move forward one step closer to the goal. The first child to cross the goal becomes the "teacher" and calls the sentences for the rest of the class.

Sentences: The carrier phrase, "I'm thinking of a ....," is completed with the animal names used in the previous activities.

LESSON TWELVE

ACTIVITY II FIXING THE CAR

Material: Blackboard, chalk. Cue words: body, front wheels, back wheels, tires, windshield, hood, trunk, fenders, roof, bumper, headlights, steering wheel.

Procedure: The children are called on individually to add the parts of the car to the sketch which is being made on the board.

Sentences: The carrier phrase, "Add a ....," to the car, is used with the cue words.

ACTIVITY II FIXING THE CAR

Material: Blackboard, chalk. Cue words: Fall, drive, knock, tire, motor, steering wheel, service station, hood, woodpecker.

Procedure: The children repeat the sentences together but are called on individually to answer the questions.

Sentences:

One Fall day, the Jones family went for a drive.
   Father Jones heard a funny knock in the car.
   Mother said it sounded like a bad tire.
   Bobby thought it might be the motor.
   Betty thought it was the steering wheel.
   Father decided to take it to a service station.

The man at the service station looked under the hood.

He laughed. It wasn't the front tire.

It wasn't the motor or the steering wheel.

A woodpecker was under the hood.

Questions:

Where were the Joneses going?

What season of the year was it?

Why was Father worried?

What did Mother, Betty and Bobby think was wrong?

What did the man at the service station find?

ACTIVITY III A CAR RACE

Material: Blackboard, chalk, small plastic car for each child. Cue words: previous auto parts plus battery, front seat, back seat, dashboard, brake, backlights, spare tire.

Procedure: Lanes are drawn vertically on the board for each car driver. Horizontal lines are drawn across the lanes to form five or six squares. The children have only one chance to repeat the sentence. The children move their cars forward one square each time until someone crosses the goal line. The winner assumes the role of "teacher" and gives the sentences to the others.

Sentences: The carrier phrase, "A car has....," is used with the cue words.

LESSON THIRTEEN

ACTIVITY I BUILDING A HOUSE

Material: Flannel board, felt figures: frame,
roof, chimney, door, windows, garage, porch,
sidewalk, tree, flowers, smoke, fence, gate, mail
box. Use the felt figures for cue words.

Procedure: The children are called on individually to add the items in order to complete
the scene.

Sentences:

First we need the frame for the house.
Next let's add the chimney to the roof.
Please put the door on the house.
Put the windows next to the door.
The front of the house should have a porch.
Put a garage beside the house.
We should have a sidewalk in front of the
house.
A tree would look nice in the yard.
Put a fence around the house and garage.
Put some flowers inside the fence.
There is smoke coming out of the chimney.
Put a mail box by the side of the door.
Put a gate in the middle of the fence.

ACTIVITY II

DECORATING THE LIVING ROOM

Material: Blackboard, chalk.   Cue   words:

painting, fireplace, wood, chair, table, lamp, couch, pillows, ash trays, flowers.

Procedure: Draw a large square to represent the living room. The children draw large sketches of the furniture mentioned in the sentences.

Sentences:

Hang a painting on the wall.

Put a fireplace beneath the painting.

Put some wood in the fireplace.

Put a big chair to the right of the fireplace.

Put a small table to the right of the chair.

Put a tall lamp on the table.

Put a couch across the room from the table.

Put some pillows on the couch.

Put small tables on either side of the couch.

Put some ash trays on the tables.

Put a long low table in front of the couch.

Put some flowers on the table.

ACTIVITY III DARTS

Material: Suction tip darts, blackboard sketches from the previous activity.

Procedure: See Lesson Seven, Activity III.

Sentences: Carrier phrase, "Throw the dart at the ...."

LESSON FOURTEEN

ACTIVITY I BUILDING ANIMALS

Material: Flannel board, felt figures of the following animals with separate heads, bodies, legs, arms, tails, etc.: a man, horse, cow, duck, rabbit, giraffe, goat. Use as cues.

Procedure: Place all of the pieces of the various animals together on a table large enough to use for putting the animals together. Establish the identity of the animal you will put together and then have the children find the parts necessary.

Sentences:

This animal lives in cities. He is the only animal that can read, write and speak. His name is Man.

Find the man's .... (parts of the man)

This animal lives on a farm. He can pull a plow or carry a man. He eats grass and oats. He can run very fast. He is a horse.

Find the horse's ....

This animal lives on a farm. She gives us milk and cheese, and butter. She eats grass. She is very big and has horns. She is a cow.

Find the cow's ....

We are going to build a bird now. This bird lives near the water and likes to swim. It sometimes lives on a farm. It is very good to eat. Let's build a picture of a duck.

Where is the duck's ....?

This is a very fast animal. He loves to eat carrots. He has long ears and a round tail. He hops instead of walking. This is a rabbit.

Can you find the rabbit's ....?

This animal lives in Africa. We see him in the zoo. He has horns on his head. He has a very long neck. Let's build a giraffe.

Give me the giraffe's ....

This animal lives on a farm. He isn't very big. He gives meat like a cow. He gives us wool for our clothes. This animal is a sheep.

Can you give me the sheep's ....?

ACTIVITY II   THE THREE BEARS

Material: Blackboard, chalk, large sheets of paper, crayons. Cue words: Mother bear, Father bear, Baby bear, Goldilocks, soup, walk, cooled, tasted, drink, living room, fast asleep.

Procedure: Have the children mark off five large squares on the front of the paper which you have given them and five squares on the back. They are to fill in each of the squares

with stick figures showing the action of each
sentence. Repeat and re-phrase as much as necessary.

Sentences:

Mother bear made some soup one day.

It was too hot. Mother bear, Father bear, and
Baby bear went for a walk while it cooled.

While they were gone, Goldilocks came to
the house.

She tasted Mother bear and Father bear's
soup.

She drank all of Baby bear's soup.

Then she sat down in the bear's chairs in the
living room.

Goldilocks broke Baby bear's chair.

Then she tried all of the beds upstairs.

She fell asleep in Baby bear's bed.

When the bears came home she ran away.

ACTIVITY III BINGO

(if there is sufficient time)

See Lesson Five, Activity III.

LESSON FIFTEEN

ACTIVITY I BUILDING A WESTERN SCENE

Material: Flannel board, felt figures: bird,
cloud, saddle, fence, apple, tree, dog, cactus,
lasso, cowboy, sun, butterfly, horse. Use felt
figures for cue words.

Procedure: The children place the two objects mentioned in the sentence in the correct positions in response to the directions.

Sentences:

A bird is flying below the clouds.

A cowboy's saddle is resting on a fence.

A tree stands next to the fence.

A red apple hangs from the tree.

A cactus is growing near the tree.

A dog is sleeping next to the cactus.

A cowboy takes down the saddle.

The cowboy holds a lasso in his left hand.

A butterfly is flying over the cowboy.

The cowboy's horse puts his head under the fence.

ACTIVITY II A TEXAS VACATION

Material: Blackboard, chalk. Cue words: vacation, trip, ocean, Texas, train, hotel, town, disappointed, Indians, lasso, laughed.

Procedure: The class answers the questions individually but responds to the sentences together.

Sentences:

Mother and Father Jones wanted to go on a vacation.

Whenever Father or Mother mentioned a place to go, Bobby and Betty shook their heads.

They asked Bobby and Betty where they wanted to go.

Betty wanted to take a trip across the ocean.

Bobby wanted to go to Texas.

The family decided to go to Texas.

They took a train to get to the West.

When they reached Texas, they went to a hotel.

Bobby and Betty took a walk through the town.

Mother and Father stayed at the hotel.

Betty and Bobby were disappointed.

The streets of the town look like their town's.

The people looked like their friends at home.

Bobby asked a man where all the cowboys and Indians were.

The man only laughed.

Then he told Bobby to look around the hotel to find the cowboys.

They walked back to the hotel.

They saw a man with western clothes and a lasso.

He was trying to lasso a fence post.

The cowboy could not get the lasso to work.

Bobby laughed at the cowboy.

The cowboy turned around to look at Bobby.

Bobby laughed harder.

The cowboy was his own father.

Questions:

Who decided to go on a vacation?

Where did Betty want to go?

Where did Bobby want to go?
Why do you think he wanted to go there?
Why was Bobby disappointed in the town?
Where did he go to see a cowboy?
Who was the cowboy?

ACTIVITY III MAKING UP A STORY

Material: Flannel board, felt figures used in Activity I.

Procedure: Each child takes four or five of the felt figures and places them on the flannel board. He then makes up a story for the others to lip read.

LESSON SIXTEEN

ACTIVITY I THE FAMILY BREAKFAST

Material: Flannel board, felt figures: table, plate, spoon, knife, fork, napkin, cereal, milk, glass, butter, toast, egg, bacon. Use felt figures for cue words.

Procedure: The children perform the appropriate activity in response to the directions.

Sentences:
Put the table on the board.
Put the plate on the table.
Put the napkin by the plate.
Put the knife, spoon and fork by the plate.
Pour the cereal into the plate.

Pour the milk into the glass.

Spread the butter on the toast.

Take the cereal away.

Wash the plate.

Put the eggs in the plate.

Put some bacon by the eggs.

Clear the plate from the table.

Clear the glass from the table.

Clear the knife, spoon and fork from the table.

Clear the crumbs away.

ACTIVITY II WHAT FOOD IS IT?

Material: Blackboard, chalk. Cue words: paper, corn, wheat, oats, sugar, milk.

Procedure: See Lesson Five, Activity I.

Sentences:

This is made of paper.

Sometimes it is very big.

Sometimes it's very small.

There is something inside of it.

What's inside may be made of corn.

What's inside may be made of wheat.

What's inside may be made of oats.

I put sugar on what's inside of it.

I pour milk on what's inside.

I see this in the morning.

I use it before I go to school.

Answer: Cereal box.

ACTIVITY III Let's Have Breakfast

Material: Table, toy dishes, silverware, utensils.

Procedure: Assign the roles of Mother, Father, Betty and Bobby Jones to the class. If there are more than four children in the group have the others play the roles of guests. The children carry on a conversation around the breakfast table without using voice.

LESSON SEVENTEEN

ACTIVITY I The Family Lunch

Material: Flannel board, felt figures: table, plate, glass, napkin, silverware, sandwich, milk, jelly, potato chips, cake, crumbs.

Procedure: See Lesson Sixteen, Activity I.

Sentences:

Put the table on the board.
Put the plate on the table.
Place the glass by the plate.
The napkin goes by the plate.
The silverware should be on either side of the plate.
Let's put a sandwich on the plate.
Pour some milk in the glass near the plate.
Put a jar of jelly on the table.
Place some potato chips next to the sandwich.
Clear the plate from the table.

Pour some more milk in the glass.
Wash the plate and put it back on the table.
Put some cake in the plate.
Clear the plate away again.
Clear the silverware away and the glass.
Wipe up the crumbs.

ACTIVITY II

Mr. Jones Takes His Lunch

Material: Blackboard, chalk. Cue words: early, sandwiches, soup, fruit, cake, cookies, newspaper, usual, package, garbage.

Procedure: The class repeats the sentences together but answer the questions individually.

Sentences:

Mother Jones always wakes up early.
She has to fix Mr. Jones his lunch.
She always makes two sandwiches and soup.
Sometimes she puts in fruit, cake, or cookies.
She wraps the lunch in a newspaper.
Mr. Jones always likes his lunch.
One day, however, he did not like his lunch.
He woke up later than usual one morning.
He did not have time for breakfast.
He had to run out of the house.
He picked up the package wrapped in newspaper.
When it was time for lunch he was very hungry.

But he had picked up the wrong package.
What do you think was inside?
He had picked up a package of garbage.

Questions:

Why did Mrs. Jones wake up early?
What did she usually fix for Mr. Jones?
Do you think he liked his lunch usually?
Why didn't he have breakfast one morning?
Do you think he was hungry that day? Why?
What was inside the package?

ACTIVITY III   LET'S HAVE LUNCH

See Lesson Sixteen, Activity III for materials
and procedure.

LESSON EIGHTEEN

ACTIVITY I   THE FAMILY DINNER

Material: Flannel board, felt figures: table,
plate, glass, napkin, silverware, meat, peas, potatoes, salad bowl, saucer, coffee cup, dessert
plate, ice cream. Use felt figures for cue
words:

Procedure: The children perform the appropriate activity in response to the directions.

Sentences:

Put the table on the board.
Put the plate on the table.
Place the glass to the left of the plate.

Place the napkin to the left of the plate.
Put the silverware around the plate.
Serve some meat in the middle of the plate.
Serve some peas to the right of the meat.
Serve some potatoes to the left of the meat.
Place the salad bowl to the left of the plate.
The saucer goes to the right of the plate.
Place the coffee cup in the saucer.
Clear the plate from the table, please.
Take the glass away from the table, please.
Take away all the silverware by the plate,
but leave the spoon.
Take the salad bowl away now.
Fill the coffee cup with coffee.
Bring a plate for the dessert.
Put some ice cream in the plate.
Clear away all the dishes.
Clean the crumbs from the table.

ACTIVITY II WHAT FOOD IS IT?

Material: Blackboard, chalk. Cue words: animal, fish, bird, wings, holiday, dressing, dark, light, people.

Procedure: See Lesson Five, Activity I.

Sentences:

I am not an animal.
I am not a fish, either.
I am a large bird you see on a farm.
I have wings but I do not fly.
People like to eat me on a holiday.

Before they eat me they stuff me with dress-ing.

Some people like my dark meat.
Other people like my light meat.

Answer: turkey.

ACTIVITY III LET'S HAVE DINNER

See Lesson Sixteen, Activity III for mater-ials and procedure.

LESSON NINETEEN

ACTIVITY I

WHAT CAN WE DO ON A PICNIC?

Material: Pictures on cards of hot dogs, boys playing catch, swimming, pop corn, swings, sliding board, sand pile.

Procedure: Each child is given a complete riddle to answer and if he does so correctly he is given the picture of that activity. No cue words are to be used but repeat and re-phrase as much as necessary.

Sentences:

We need a fire to do this.
We need buns to put these in.
We are cooking something named for an animal.

Answer: hot dogs.

We need two people for this.
We need a glove for one person.
We need a bat and a ball for the other.

Answer: playing baseball.

We can do this all by ourselves.
We need a special suit for this.
We do this in the water.

Answer: swimming.

We should have a fire to do this.
We need corn kernels and butter.
We need a pan on a long handle.

Answer: popping pop corn.

We need a piece of wood and chains for this.
We need a tree to tie the chains to.
We need plenty of room to go up and down.

Answer: swinging.

We should have a long ladder for this.
We need a long piece of shiny metal.
One end is high in the air while the other is touching the ground.

Answer: sliding.

We should have a big box for this.
It must have something soft in it.
We can make roads and castles in the box.

Answer: playing in a sand box.

ACTIVITY II

THE JONES FAMILY GOES ON A PICNIC

Material: Blackboard, chalk. Cue words: car, picnic grounds, food basket, tablecloth, shook her finger, pickles, cake.

Procedure: Each child is given a role to act out in the story. Use imaginary objects, furniture, etc. If there are more than five children have the others play the parts of friends and make up additional sentences.

Sentences:

Mother, Father, Betty, Bobby and Sparky wanted to go on a picnic.

They all got dressed up to go on the picnic.

Even Sparky put on his collar and blanket.

They got into the car and drove to the picnic grounds.

When they reached the picnic grounds, Father and Bobby brought out the food basket.

Mother and Betty put a tablecloth on the table.

Sparky put his nose in the food basket.

Betty shook her finger at Sparky.

Mother put a large jar of pickles on the table.

Father put a big dish of potato salad on the table.

Bobby put a pitcher of lemonade on the table.

Sparky jumped up on the table.

Betty took Sparky down from the table.

Everyone put food on their plates.

Everyone poured lemonade in their glasses.

Everyone ate their food and drank their lemonade.

Mother put some food on the ground for Sparky.

Sparky did not eat any of the food.

When they had finished, Mother looked in the basket for the cake.

It was gone.

Sparky started to crawl away. Then he ran.

That was why Sparky wasn't hungry! He had eaten the cake.

ACTIVITY III

CHARADES — GAMES WE PLAY ON A PICNIC

Material: Slips of paper with the following activities written on them: fishing, swimming, eating, playing ball, dancing, playing ping pong, swinging, sliding.

Procedure: Each child picks a slip of paper with the activity written on it to act out without using verbal clues. The others ask questions of the performer without using voice.

USE OF VOICE

The remaining lessons in the *Primary Lessons* section of this book are to be given, using a soft

voice in order to allow the children to synthesize visual *and* some auditory clues. This more
closely approximates normal verbal communication than does the silent presentation of practice
sentences; it is felt that the silent presentation
of sentences enables the hard of hearing child to
develop maximally those skills necessary for the
visual component of verbal communication.
However, the child must learn to use both the
auditory and visual clues after developing opti-
mum skills in each separately lip reading and
auditory training. In both the *Primary and
Intermediate* sections the final lessons have been
designed to relate these aspects of communication.

LESSON TWENTY

ACTIVITY I WHAT DO WE DO IN SCHOOL?

Material: Blackboard, chalk. Cue words:
spelling, reading, writing, art class, singing, recess.

Procedure: The riddle is told in its entirety
before allowing the child whose turn it is to
guess the answer.

Sentences:

We have to have a pencil and paper to do this.
We have to listen to the teacher.
We have to get all the letters in a word.

Answer: spelling.

We have to have paint and paper for this.
Sometimes we use crayons instead of paint.
We have to look at flowers or people for this.

Answer: art class.

We have to look at a book to do this.
We have to do this aloud sometimes.
We have to do this silently sometimes.

Answer: reading.

We have to listen to a piano when we do this.
Boys who do this sound different from girls.
We have to do this aloud.

Answer: singing.

We have to have a pencil and paper for this.
Sometimes we tell a story this way.
Sometimes we do our homework this way.

Answer: writing.

I think you like this best of all.
All you have to do is play outside.
You have to stay inside when it rains.

Answer: recess.

ACTIVITY II

BOBBY JONES MAKES A MISTAKE

Material: Blackboard, chalk. Cue words:

woke up, fishing pole, books, school, got up, make up.

Procedure: The group repeats the sentences together but the questions are answered individually.

Sentences:

Bobby woke up very late one morning.

He looked out of the window.

The sun was shining very brightly.

Bobby got up and washed his hands and face.

Then he went to his closet to get some clothes.

When he opened the closet door, guess what he saw.

He saw his fishing pole standing in the corner.

Bobby looked at his school books waiting on the desk.

He didn't want to go to school on such a fine day.

He took his fishing pole and went out the back door.

No one saw him leave to go fishing.

He came back home at four o'clock and hid his fishing pole.

He was going to make up a story about what he did in school.

No one was home.

He saw a note on the table.

The note said, "Sorry you had to go away.

Father has taken us all to the *Saturday* baseball game!"

Questions:

Was it a nice day when Bobby woke up?

What did he do when he got out of bed?

What did he see on the desk?

What did he see in the closet?

Where did Bobby go?

What did he do with his fishing pole when he came home?

What was he going to make up?

Where was everyone when he got home?

What was Bobby's mistake?

ACTIVITY III BOUNCE BALL

THINGS I SEE IN SCHOOL

Material: Large rubber ball. No cue words are used.

Procedure: The children are instructed to think of all the things they might see in school such as books, desks, blackboards, etc. They then form a circle with about three feet between each of them. The child holding the ball names an item he sees in school and bounces the ball to the first one shouting out the correct item.

Sentences: The carrier phrase, "I see a ...." in school, is used with objects around the school.

LESSON TWENTY ONE

ACTIVITY I WHERE SHOULD WE PUT IT?

Material: Flannel board, felt figures: cloud, bee, flower, sun, grass, rainbow, bird, boat, flag, boy, man, dog, cat, chair, hat. Use the felt figures for cue words.

Procedure: Mix all of the felt figures together on a large table. The child whose turn it is picks out the proper object and places it as directed on the board. As each scene is completed, remove the figures and place them with the others.

Sentences: *On* and *In*

Put the cloud on the flannel board.
Put the sun in the sky.
Put the grass on the flannel board.
Put a flower in the grass.
Put a bee on the flower.
Put a rainbow in the sky.
Put a bird on the rainbow.

Under and *Over*

Put the sun over the rainbow.
Put a boat under the rainbow.
Put some water under the boat.
Put a fish under the boat.
Put a flag over the boat.

Behind and *In Front Of*

Put a boy behind a man.

Put a dog in front of the man.
Put a tree behind the dog.
Put a cat in front of the tree.
Put a bird in front of the dog.

On, In, Under, Over, Behind, In Front Of

Put a man in a chair.
Put a hat on his head.
Put a bird on the hat.
Put some grass under his feet.
Put a flower in the grass.
Put a rainbow behind him.
Put the sun over him.
Put the flag in the bird's mouth.

ACTIVITY II   BETTY GETS LOST

Material: Blackboard, chalk, construction paper cut-out of Betty Jones.

Procedure: Draw a complicated maze of through streets and dead end streets. Draw simple sketches of the objects studied in Activity I along the streets at junction points. Instruct the child at the board to move Betty in some direction (up, down, under, over, below, above, around, in front of) to get her out of the maze. When the child takes a wrong direction, another member of the class takes his place until Betty is finally out. The direction is given only once with no re-phrasing.

Sentences: up above
                  down below
                  around
    Move Betty   over
                  below   } the ....
                  above
                  behind
                  in front of

ACTIVITY III   HUMAN TIC TAC TOE

Material: Chalk.

Procedure: Draw a large tic tac toe board on the floor with chalk. Draw the objects or place the felt figures of Activity I in each square. That square then becomes termed the "rainbow" or "sun" square. Select two of the class to "move" two others within the squares. A player within the squares must keep his feet or hands within a square to indicate that it is already taken. Directions are given by the children in a soft voice.

Sentences: Carrier phrase,

    Move a foot { hand
                { foot to the ....square.

LESSON TWENTY TWO

ACTIVITY I   WHAT COLOR IS IT?

Material: None. No cue words are given.

Procedure: The children are called on individually to guess the color and name of the object in the riddle.

Sentences:

This is something sweet and round.
It grows in a tall tree.
Most people like it in a pie.

Answer: an apple.

This is a very big animal.
He has a long trunk and a short tail.
We see him in the circus or at the zoo.

Answer: an elephant.

This is something big and round.
It grows on the ground on the farm.
We like to eat it in a pie on Thanksgiving.

Answer: a pumpkin.

This is something very tall.
Children love to climb in it.
Fruit grows on it.

Answer: a tree.

This is not an animal but it has a tail.
It has no wings but it flies in the air.
Boys fly it on the end of a string.

Answer: a kite.

This is something round and hot.

It moves across the sky in the daytime.

It goes away at night.

The plants grow tall because of it.

Answer: the sun.

ACTIVITY II COLOR SKETCH

Material: Crayon, paper. Cue words: red, orange, yellow, green, blue, purple, brown, black, white.

Procedure: Each child is given a piece of paper and a box of crayons. The class is to draw a scene in which they will use all of the above colors following the directions in the sentences.

Sentences:

Draw a black border all the way around your paper.

Draw a green line across the middle of the page. Fill in the grass with your green crayon.

Draw a brown tree with green leaves.

Put red apples all over the tree.

Draw a beautiful yellow sun up in the sky.

Draw a white cloud below the sun.

Color the rest of the sky a light blue.

Draw some orange birds in the sky.

Draw some red apples on the ground.

Draw a purple worm eating the apples.

ACTIVITY III DARTS

Material: Suction tip darts, large color wheels containing the colors in Activity II.

Procedure: See Lesson Seven, Activity III.

LESSON TWENTY THREE

ACTIVITY I WHERE MAY I FIND IT?

Material: Blackboard, chalk, dollhouse, doll furniture. Cue words: living room, bed room, kitchen, dining room, bathroom. If there are additional rooms needed for other children, make up sentences about the closet and basement.

Procedure: Assign each child a room which he will fill with furniture by saying the name of his room whenever you mention an object which belongs in it. If an object might go in two rooms, give it to the one calling his room name first.

Sentences: The carrier phrase, "In which room does the .... belong," is used with all of the doll furniture.

ACTIVITY II

MOTHER JONES PAINTS THE KITCHEN FLOOR

Material: Blackboard, chalk. Cue words: paint, brush, kitchen, upstairs, bathroom, cleaned, angry, laughed, corner.

Procedure: The class answers the questions as individuals but repeats the sentences together.

Sentences:

Mother Jones wanted to paint the kitchen floor.

She went to the basement to get some paint and the brush.

She brought the paint and brush upstairs.

She took the brush to the bathroom to wash it.

Father Jones had not cleaned the brush.

Mother was very angry. "Men are not very good painters" she said.

Then she took the paint can into the kitchen.

She opened it and was angry again.

Bobby Jones had let some red paint get in the blue paint can.

"Men are not very good painters at all!" she said.

She began to paint the floor.

She was almost finished when Bobby came home.

She said, "Women are much better painters than men."

Bobby looked in the kitchen and laughed.

Then Father Jones came home from work.

Mother said, "Women are much better painters than men."

Father laughed. He said, "We are good enough. We never paint ourselves into corners."

Mother had to wait until the paint dried to get out of the kitchen.

Questions:

What was Mother going to do?
Why was she angry with Bobby?
Why was she angry with Father?
Where did she clean the brush?
What did she say to Bobby and Father?
Why did they laugh?
How did she get out of the room?
How would you have painted the room?

ACTIVITY III CHECKER TOSS

Material: Dollhouse, checkers for each child.

Procedure: The children are instructed to toss their checkers into one of the rooms. If they get it in the right room they receive two points; if they get it in any room except the one named, they receive one point. The first to reach ten points becomes the "teacher" and calls the directions for the others.

Sentences: Use the carrier phrase, "Toss the checker into the .... room."

LESSON TWENTY FOUR

ACTIVITY I TRUE OR FALSE

Material: None.

Procedure: The children are asked individually to judge a statement to be true or false. The statement is given just once and if the child misses, the same statement is given to the next person.

Sentences:

A fish is *larger than* a spider.
A cow is larger than an elephant.
A book is larger than a potato chip.
A bee is larger than a toothbrush.
A boat is larger than a mountain.
A fly is larger than a football.
A basketball is larger than a cookie.
A thimble is larger than a table.

A shirt is *smaller than* a ship.
A broom is smaller than a watch.
A leg is smaller than a head.
A hot dog is smaller than a toothpick.
A plate is smaller than a glass.
A sandwich is smaller than a swing.
A chair is smaller than a house.
A mother is smaller than a car.

A pencil is *longer than* a watch.
A table is longer than a chair.
A hotel is longer than a cowboy.
A hat is longer than a coat.
A train is longer than a dog.
A tree is longer than an apple.
A fish is longer than a giraffe.
A crayon is longer than a blackboard.
A paint brush is longer than a living room.

ACTIVITY II BOBBY LEARNS A LESSON

Material: Blackboard, chalk. Cue words: new
boy, age, questions, Tom, Bobby Jones, older,
taller, faster, higher, farther, rock, Little
League.

Procedure: The children answer questions individually but repeat the sentences together.

Sentences:

One day, a new boy moved into town.

He was just Bobby Jones' age.

Bobby met him on the way to school one day.

He asked the new boy many questions.

Bobby asked, "What's your name?"

The new boy said his name was Tom.

"I bet I'm older than you." Bobby said.

They were the same age.

"I bet I can run faster than you," Bobby
bragged to Tom.

They had a race and it was a tie.

"I'm taller than you." Bobby said.

They turned out to be the same height.

"I can throw farther than you," Bobby bragged again.

Bobby picked up a rock and threw it as far
as he could.

It landed close to the fence around the park.

Tom picked up a rock and threw it.

It went very high into the air.

It went higher than Bobby's; it went faster than Bobby's; it went far past the fence.

Tom was a pitcher with the Little League.

Questions:

Where did Bobby meet the new boy?
Who was older?
Who was taller?
Who was faster?
Who was bragging?
How far did Bobby throw his rock?
How far did Tom throw his?

ACTIVITY III   TWENTY QUESTIONS

Material: Objects in the room. Sample questions on board.

Procedure: One of the children picks an object in the room. The others ask no more than twenty questions (using a soft voice) trying to guess the object. Whoever guesses the object picks another one which the others try to guess.

Sentences: The following sentences are samples and are written on the board:

Is it bigger than a ....?
Is it smaller than a ....?
Is it taller than a ....?
Is it shorter than a .... ?
Is it higher than a ....?

INTERMEDIATE
LESSONS

LESSON ONE

ACTIVITY I INSIDE OR OUTSIDE

Material: Blackboard, chalk, slot chart, name cards for Inside and Outside, ten pictures representing the activities below. Cue words: ride, eat, watch, roller-skate, sleep, play, go, wash, mow, read.

Procedure: When the children answer the questions correctly they take the picture showing the action given in the sentence and place it under the proper name card on the slot chart.

(No voice is to be used in these lessons until Lesson Eighteen.)

Sentences:

I'm going to ride my bike. Shall I do it inside or outside?

I'm going to eat some pie. Shall I do it inside or outside?

I'm going to watch television. Shall I do it inside or outside?

I'm going to go rollerskating. Shall I do it inside or outside?

I'm going to sleep. Shall I do it inside or outside?

I'm going to play baseball. Shall I do it inside or outside?

I'm going to go fishing. Shall I do it inside or outside?

I'm going to wash the dishes. Shall I do it inside or outside?

I'm going to mow the lawn. Shall I do it inside or outside?

I'm going to read a book. Shall I do it inside or outside?

ACTIVITY II FIND THE PICTURE

Material: Pictures used in Activity I.

Procedure: Each child hides a picture used in the previous activity and then selects some other child to find the picture. The one who hid the picture gives a brief description of it and directions to its location. The picture should be hidden in an easily reached area and should be *inside* or *outside* of some familiar object.

Sentences: (Example)

I hid a picture of a boy sleeping. Go to the back of the room. Now turn around and touch the wall. Next put your hands above your head. The picture is inside a hat on the shelf.

ACTIVITY III

THE TURTLE AND THE RABBIT

Material: The only materials to be used in all of the Fables are the blackboard and chalk for the cue words. The only *material* to be

listed in the succeeding lessons will be the cue
words.

Cue words: rabbit, animal, forest, race, turtle,
crawled, sleeping.

Procedure: Since the *procedure* for all of the
succeeding fables will be identical, it will be
described just this one time.

Each statement is given as often as necessary
to all the children together who repeat it when
they think they have the meaning. Emphasize
that there is nothing wrong in *guessing* the
meaning even if they do not know all the words
in a sentence. The questions are to be answered
individually and are also repeated and re-
phrased until understood.

Sentences:

Once there was a very fast rabbit.

He bragged that he was the fastest animal in
the forest.

One day he said, "Nobody can beat me in a
race."

Just then the turtle said, "I'd like to try."

They got ready to race under a tree.

The rabbit raced away as fast as he could.

The turtle crawled along very slowly.

The rabbit looked behind him and could not
even see the turtle.

He laughed and sat down under a tree to take
a rest.

He fell asleep laughing at the turtle.

While he was sleeping, the turtle crawled slowly past.

The rabbit was still sleeping when the turtle won the race.

Moral: Slow but sure wins the race.

Questions:

Who bragged that he was the fastest animal in the forest?

How did he want to show that he was fast?
Who offered to race with the rabbit?
Where did they start the race?
Could the turtle run faster than the rabbit?
Why did the rabbit lose the race?
What does the moral of the story mean?

ACTIVITY IV CHARADES

Material: Ten pictures used in Activity I and II.

Procedure: Each child selects a picture used in Activity I to act out without using verbal clues. The others ask questions without voice to guess the action represented.

LESSON TWO

ACTIVITY I DO WE CARRY IT OR WEAR IT?

Material: Flannel board; felt figures: umbrella, hat, shoes, purse, basket, kite, mittens, book, socks, box, ring; name cards entitled Wear It and Carry It.

Procedure: Make two columns on the flannel board heading one with the name card Wear It and the other with Carry It. Give the sentences individually and have the child called on put the object mentioned in the right column.

Sentences:

Mother took her umbrella because it was raining.

Father's hat was lying on the table.

My feet hurt because my shoes are new.

My sister bought a new leather purse.

My brother put the eggs in the basket.

She bought a new dress for the dance.

They went outside to fly their kite.

We wear mittens to keep our hands warm in winter.

I like to read a good book.

His socks are too big for his feet.

You should keep a box of food in the kitchen.

Her ring was too big for her finger.

ACTIVITY II FIND THE PICTURE

Material: Felt figures used in Activity I.

Procedure: See Lesson One, Activity II.

ACTIVITY III

THE OLD MAN AND HIS SONS

Cue words: several, fought, speak, unhappy, bundle of sticks, string, break, lesson.

Sentences:

An old man had several sons who always fought.

They would fight and then not speak to each other.

This made their father very unhappy.

One day he decided to teach them a lesson.

He tied a bundle of sticks together with string.

He told each of the boys to try to break the bundle of sticks.

No one was able to do it.

Then he took the string off the bundle.

He showed the boys that he could break all of the sticks one by one.

Moral: Together you win, divided you lose.

Questions:

How many sons did the old man have?

Why was the old man unhappy?

What would his sons do after they fought?

What did he use to teach them a lesson?

Were the boys able to break the bundle of sticks?

What did the old man do after taking the string off the bundle?

What is the moral of the story?

ACTIVITY IV FISHING

Material: Horseshoe magnet attached to string, felt figures used in Activity I with paper clips attached. Use felt figures for cue words.

Procedure: Each child takes his turn fishing for a felt figure with the magnet. He then describes the figure to the class which tries to guess its name. The child guessing the most objects wins.

LESSON THREE

ACTIVITY I WHAT IS MY OCCUPATION?

Material: Pictures of a mother, teacher, father, mailman, milkman, grocery clerk, policeman, fireman, dentist. These are mounted on heavy construction paper. Use these pictures for cue words.

Procedure: The sentences describing the various occupations are given individually and when the child repeats his sentences, he is permitted to scotch-tape the picture to the blackboard.

Sentences:

I'm someone who wakes you every morning.
I cook your meals and wash your clothes.
Who am I?

Answer: mother.

I'm someone you see in school everyday.
I help you learn to read and write.
Who am I?

Answer: teacher.

I'm someone you see only in the morning and in the evening.

I make money so you can eat and have nice clothes to wear.

Who am I?

Answer: father.

I come to your house everyday to bring you letters.

I wear a gray suit and carry a big leather bag.

Who am I?

Answer: mailman.

I come to your house early in the morning.

I bring you fresh white milk each day.

Who am I?

Answer: milkman.

I weigh food for your mother at the store.

I also take her money when she is ready to leave.

Who am I?

Answer: grocery clerk.

You can find me any time of day or night.

I stand on the corner and direct traffic .

Who am I?

Answer: policeman.

I ride in a bright red truck.
I always help when there's a fire.
Who am I?

Answer: fireman.

When you come to see me I make you feel better.

When you go away you sometimes leave your tooth.

Who am I?

Answer: dentist.

ACTIVITY II WHO IS IT?

Material: Blackboard, chalk.

Procedure: Draw five columns of ten numbers each on the board using the numbers from one through fifty (i.e.; first column, one to ten; second column, eleven through twenty, etc.) Connect any two numbers each time one of the sentences is lip read correctly by the class. The class is to guess the object you are drawing.

Sentences:

I live in a large house.
I just work a few times each day.
I wish I didn't have to work at all.
I do a lot of driving when I work.
Sometimes I get very wet when I work.
I must be very brave when I go to work.
I climb tall ladders when I work.

People are not very happy when I go to work.

But they would be unhappy if I did not come to work.

When I work I am very warm.

My truck is bright red.

Answer: fireman.

ACTIVITY III

THE WOLF IN SHEEP'S CLOTHING

Cue words: hungry, catch, chased, shepherd, sheepskin, tied, growled, baaa.

Sentences:

Everyday, the hungry wolf tried to catch a sheep to eat.

The shepherd always chased the wolf away.

One day, the wolf found an old sheepskin lying on the ground.

He tied it around his body and covered his head.

Then he went walking along with the sheep.

He still did not catch any sheep that day.

The shepherd caught the wolf and killed him.

The shepherd knew it was the wolf because it growled. It did not say "Baaa."

Moral: You can't always tell what something is just by looking at it.

Questions:

Why did the wolf want to catch a sheep?

Why didn't the wolf catch any sheep?

What did the wolf find lying on the ground?
What did the wolf do with the sheepskin?
Did the wolf catch any sheep that day?
What happened to the wolf?
How did the shepherd know it was a wolf?
What is the moral of the story?

ACTIVITY IV DARTS

Material: Suction tip darts, each of which is a different color; blackboard and chalk.

Procedure: Draw circle figures of the various workers in Activity I or use the pictures which have been scotch-taped to the blackboard as targets at which the children throw their darts. Each hit is worth one point. The first one to reach a score of ten commands the others.

Sentences: Throw the dart at the ....

LESSON FOUR

ACTIVITY I WHERE WOULD YOU BUY IT?

Material: Blackboard, chalk. Cue words: drugstore, grocery, furniture store, hardware store, bookstore, flower shop, dime store, shoe store, department store, bakery.

Procedure: Make a column of the cue words on the board. When the children have repeated the sentences correctly, they are to draw the object purchased next to the store from which it was obtained.

Sentences:

I bought a loaf of bread from the bakery.

You can buy toys at the dime store for a nickel, a dime, or a dollar.

She bought a chair and couch from the furniture store.

We buy our vegetables at the grocery store around the corner.

They all went to the drugstore for a soda after the dance.

My father buys his screws, bolts and nails at the hardware store.

Your shoes come from a shoe store.

Her boy friend sent her flowers from the flower shop.

His teacher told the class to buy a new book at the bookstore.

Our family went shopping for some clothes in a department store.

ACTIVITY II

SHOPPING IN THE DEPARTMENT STORE

Material: Five or six articles in the classroom which could be purchased at a department store.

Procedure: This is essentially a creative dramatics situation and the action should develop normally from the interests of the class. Each child is assigned a role of cashier, clerk and customer, and general instructions are given to inquire about the cost and quality of the object to be purchased.

ACTIVITY III   THE FOX AND THE GRAPES

Cue words: hot, grapes, hanging, juiciest, high, jumped, hurt, angrily, sour, weather.

Sentences:

A fox was walking through the forest one hot day.

He was hungry and thirsty because it was so warm.

He walked underneath the branches of a tree and looked up.

He saw a beautiful big bunch of grapes hanging from the branch.

He began to lick his lips.

"Those are the juiciest, best looking grapes I've seen."

He jumped up to bite the bunch of grapes.

He could not jump high enough to bite them.

He backed away from the tree and then ran toward it.

He jumped again and tried to bite the grapes.

He missed one more time.

He fell on his back and hurt himself.

When he got up, every bone in his body hurt.

Even his mouth hurt from licking his lips too much.

He walked away without looking up at the grapes.

"Oh well," he said angrily, "They're probably very sour anyway."

Moral: It's easy to find excuses for things we can't do.

Questions:

Where was the fox walking?

How was the weather that day?

What did he see in a tree?

How many times did he try to get the grapes?

What happened the second time he tried to get the grapes?

Was he happy or unhappy?

What did he say when he missed the grapes again?

What is the moral of the story?

ACTIVITY IV   STEP FORWARD PLEASE

(Grocery Shopping)

Material: None.

Procedure: Line the class against one wall and mark a goal line about six feet from the wall. The children are to move forward one step each time they successfully repeat the sentence given until one of them crosses the goal. The first child crossing the goal becomes the "teacher" and selects any type of store about which he wishes to give sentences.

Sentences:

>   some ⎫
> I bought a   ⎬ .... at the grocery store.
>   the ⎭

LESSON FIVE

ACTIVITY I TRANSPORTATION

Material: Pictures of a wagon, airplane, bus, car, bicycle, train, truck and horse. Use these pictures for the cue words.

Procedure: Each child answers a riddle by selecting the right picture from the table and by giving its name. Repeat or re-phrase as much as necessary but do not continue until the child and the rest of the class can answer.

Sentences:

We took a trip to the city. We caught this form of transportation on the corner. When we got on, a conductor took our money. How did we go?

Answer: bus.

I went to the store. My form of transportation had two tires and pedals. I sat on a small seat. How did I go?

Answer: bicycle.

I went around the farm in this. There were

people in the front and animals in the back. It had four wheels. How did I go?

Answer: truck.

I went on a trip to the country. I rode there in this form of transportation. My Daddy drives this to work. How did I go?

Answer: car.

I went for a trip in the sky. This form of transportation had wings and jets. It went faster than any other kind of transportation. How did I go?

Answer: airplane.

I took a trip across the country. I went in something long and shiny. It ran on tracks and stopped in big cities. How did I go?

Answer: train.

I went from my house to the corner. I rode in something very small. It had four tires and a handle. It was painted red. How did I go?

Answer: wagon.

I went on a trip through the park. I rode on something taller than a man. It had four legs and a tail. It had a saddle. How did I go?

Answer: horse.

ACTIVITY II

A SIGHT-SEEING TRIP IN YOUR TOWN

Material: List the names of the tallest building, largest department store, furniture store, clothing store, and supermarket in your own town.

Procedure: All the children arrange their chairs in single file as if they were in a sight-seeing bus. The child in the front chair is the driver and the teacher pretends to be a tourist guide. The children repeat the sentences together.

Sentences:

Good afternoon.

Today we are going to take a trip through our town (city, village).

We will drive through the city and see all of the places we know.

Driver, would you please take a left turn.

Look at all the tall buildings.

The tallest building you see is the ....

Do you see that big building with all the doors and glass windows?

That is the .... department store.

Driver, please take a right turn now.

Do you see that building with the large sign and the furniture in the windows?

That is the .... furniture store where mother buys her chairs and beds.

That building right next door to it is the

.... clothing store where Father buys his suits and hats.

Driver, would you please turn the bus around now?

Notice that long building with all the people coming out. That is the .... grocery store where you do your shopping.

Well, this is the end of the line.

I hope you enjoyed your trip.

ACTIVITY III

THE LION AND THE KIND MAN

Cue words: young, forest, sound, crying, licking, paw, gratefully, growled, afraid, thorn, bear, branch, killed, kindness, repaid.

Sentences:

Once a young man was walking through the forest.

He heard the sound of crying coming from behind some trees.

He saw a young lion licking its paw.

At first the lion growled at him because it was afraid.

He walked bravely to the lion and lifted its paw.

There was a large thorn between its toes.

The young man sat on the ground and took the thorn out of the paw.

The lion stood up and looked at him gratefully.

Then the lion walked slowly into the forest and the young man walked out of the forest.

Many years later the same man was walking through the forest again.

Now he was an old man and very weak.

All of a sudden, a big bear jumped in front of him.

The bear came slowly toward him.

Just then, the old man heard a roar.

A big lion leaped from the branch of a tree and killed the bear.

It was the same lion that the man had helped when he was young.

Moral: Kindness is often repaid with kindness.

Questions:

What was the young man doing in the forest?

What did he hear?

What did he see?

What did the lion do?

Why did the lion growl at him?

What was the matter with the lion?

What did the young man do?

What animal jumped in front of the old man?

Where was the lion?

What did the lion do?

When had the lion and the old man met before?

What is the moral of the story?

ACTIVITY IV BINGO

Material: Bingo game.

Procedure: This is played as one usually plays Bingo but no voice is used. The first one to complete his card becomes the caller.

LESSON SIX

ACTIVITY I DIFFERENT HOUSES

Material: Slot chart and name cards for an igloo, farm house, apartment house, castle, tepee, houseboat, stilt house. Cue words: Eskimo, farmer, doctor, king, Indian, sailor, pigmy; use house name cards for cue words also.

Procedure: As the children identify the house being described, they place the name card for that house in a slot on the chart.

Sentences:

I live in the North where it is cold.
I am an Eskimo.
My house is made of ice and snow. In which house do I live?

Answer: igloo.

I live in the country among the fields.
I am a farmer.
My house is big and white and stands near a red barn. In which house do I live?

Answer: farmhouse.

I live in the city among many people.
I am a doctor.
My house is small and there are many like it in the same building. In which house do I live?

Answer: apartment house.

I live in England.
I am a king.
I live in a very big house and have many servants. In which house do I live?

Answer: castle.

I live in the forests of America.
I am an Indian.
I live in a tent made of animal skins.
In which house do I live?

Answer: tepee.

I live in a house that floats on water.
I am a sailor.
My family lives with me in this floating house.
Where do I live?

Answer: houseboat.

I live in a house above the water but my house doesn't float.
I am a pigmy.
My house is on stilts so I won't get wet.
In which house do I live?

Answer: stilt house.

ACTIVITY II North Pole Sketch

Material: Blackboard, colored chalk. Cue words: Eskimo, igloo, square, seal, hole, harpoon.

Procedure: All the children stand at the board and sketch the North Pole scene from your directions. They repeat the sentence before starting the object or action in each statement.

Sentences:

Draw a picture of an Eskimo.
He has a coat with a fur collar.
He has high boots on his feet.
He wears a hood over his head.
He is standing on the ice.
One hand is raised high in the air.

Draw a picture of an igloo beside him.
The igloo is made of squares of ice.
There is a square hole in it for a door.
There is a hole in the top with smoke coming from it.

The Eskimo is holding a harpoon in his hand above his head.
The harpoon has a long point.
The harpoon is pointed toward the ice.

Draw a hole in the ice.
There is blue water in the hole.
There is a seal on the ice beside the hole.

Who would like to tell a story about the Eskimo and the seal?

ACTIVITY III

THE CROW AND THE PITCHER

Cue words: dry, dusty, road, thirsty, beak, bottom, short, suddenly, pebble, one at a time.

Sentences:

A crow was walking along a dry, dusty road.

He had not had any water for days.

He was very thirsty.

All of a sudden he saw a pitcher lying in the road.

He hopped to it very quickly and put his beak in the pitcher.

He could not reach the water in the bottom of the pitcher.

His beak was too short and the pitcher was too long.

He could not pick it up and drink it because he had no arms.

He suddenly thought of a way to get the water.

He dropped a pebble in the pitcher. He dropped another pebble into the pitcher.

Everytime he dropped a pebble in, the water rose a little higher.

Finally, it was high enough to drink.

It took a long time to get the water but it saved his life.

Moral: Do your job a little at a time and it will finally be finished.

Questions:

Where was the crow walking?

Why was he so thirsty?

What did he see lying in the road?

Was there any water in the pitcher?

Why couldn't the crow drink the water at first?

Why did he drop pebbles into the water?

What is the moral of the story?

ACTIVITY IV BOUNCE BALL

Material: Large rubber ball and the name cards from Activity I: igloo, farm house, apartment house, house boat, castle, tepee, stilt house.

Procedure: Each child is given one name card to wear on a string around his neck. The class forms a semi-circle with the teacher in the center. Instructions are given to throw the ball to the various "houses." When one of the children throws the ball to the wrong house, he is eliminated. The last child remaining becomes the "teacher" and gives the directions.

Sentences:

Throw the ball to the .... (house).

LESSON SEVEN

ACTIVITY I DIFFERENT GAMES

Material: Pictures of boys and girls playing baseball, horseshoes, hockey, football, basketball, badminton, kickball, volleyball, polo. Use these for cues.

Procedure: Each child answers the riddle by selecting the right picture from the table and giving its name. Repeat or re-phrase as much as necessary but do not go on until that child and all the others can answer the riddle.

Sentences:

To play this game we need bases, a ball and a bat to hit the ball.

Answer: baseball.

To play this game we need two stakes, two people and four iron shoes.

Answer: horseshoes.

To play this game we need a puck, a stick and lots of ice.

Answer: hockey.

To play this game we need a ball made of pig skin, a pair of goal posts and twenty two men.

Answer: football.

To play this game we need ten men, a hoop, a large rubber ball and a court.

Answer: basketball.

To play this game we need a net, two rackets and a ball that looks like a bird.

Answer: badminton.

To play this game we need a large rubber ball, bases and strong shoes to kick the ball.

Answer: kickball.

To play this game we need a net, a large ball and boys to volley the ball.

Answer: volleyball.

To play this game you need long clubs, a wooden ball and horses to ride.

Answer: polo.

ACTIVITY II

DRAWING THE MAN WHO PLAYS THE GAME

Material: Blackboard, chalk.

Procedure: Draw a large circle figure of a man. The children raise their hands to indicate that they know the object or article of clothing in the sentence. They then draw that item on the figure. The one getting the most items draws the second figure and makes up sentences for the class to lip read.

This man is going to play a game.
He needs a hat because he plays in the sun.

He uses a glove to catch balls.

He wears a shirt with short sleeves.

And of course he wears a pair of pants that are tight at the knees.

He wears socks that come up to his knees.

He uses spiked shoes to run.

He catches a small, hard ball.

He needs a bat to hit the ball.

This man is a ball player.

ACTIVITY III

THE FOX AND THE CROW

Cue words: forest, flying, cheese, branch, hungry, attention, proudly, laughing.

Sentences:

Once a hungry crow was flying through the forest.

He was looking for something to eat.

He saw a piece of cheese that a farmer had dropped while walking through the forest.

He flew to the ground and picked up the cheese.

Then he flew to the top of a branch with his cheese.

A fox walking through the forest saw the crow.

He was hungry too.

He said to the crow, "May I taste your cheese?"

The crow kept eating and paid no attention to the fox.

The fox grew hungrier.

He asked, "May I just smell your cheese, Mr. Crow?"

The crow kept eating the cheese.

Then the fox thought of a way to get the cheese.

"People say you have a beautiful, fine voice, Mr. Crow. Would you sing for me?"

The crow was very proud of his fine voice.

He opened his mouth to sing and the cheese fell to the ground.

The fox ran away with the cheese, laughing at the crow.

Questions:

Where was the crow flying?

What did the crow find?

Where did he fly to eat the cheese?

Who saw the crow in the tree?

What did the fox ask the first time?

What did he ask the second time?

What happened when the crow began to sing?

What did the fox do?

Who can make up a moral for the story?

ACTIVITY IV CHARADES ABOUT GAMES

Material: Pictures from Activity I.

Procedure: See Lesson One, Activity IV, Intermediate.

LESSON EIGHT

ACTIVITY I How Many Are There?

Material: Pencil and paper for each child. Cue words: numbers one through twenty five; numbers 5, 12, 50, 2, 5280, 4, 16, 100, 26, 12; words: dozen, pair, century, ounces, pound, inches, foot, feet, mile, letters, alphabet, oceans, world, states, United States.

Procedure: Write the numbers, 5, 12, 50, 2, 5280, 4, 16, 100, 26, 12 on the board. As the children answer the questions individually, erase the corresponding number on the board.

Sentences:

How many are there in a dozen?
How many are there in a pair?
How many legs does a cat have?
How many years are there in a century?
How many ounces are there in a pound?
How many letters are there in the alphabet?
How many inches are there in a foot?
How many feet are there in a mile?
How many oceans are there in the world?
How many states are there in the United States?

ACTIVITY II How Much is This?

Material: Pencil and paper for each child. Cue words: and=+, minus= —, times=x.

Procedure: Explain the symbols for *and, minus,* and *times.* The problems are to be given only once and the answers are to be given aloud after each problem.

Sentences:

How much are:
10+1, 9+2, 8+3, 7+4, 6+5, 5+6?

How much are:
1+3, 2+5, 4+6, 8+1, 7+3, 9+0?

How much is:
5—1, 4—2, 3—0, 6—6, 9—8, 8—7?

How much is:
2x2, 3x3, 4x2, 5x4, 6x3, 7x2?

ACTIVITY III

THE BOY WHO CRIED WOLF

Cue words: shepherd, field, lonely, visit, pretending, screamed, liar, truth, village.

Sentences:

Once there was a young shepherd boy.

He watched sheep every day for the village farmers.

He watched the sheep in a field that was far from the village.

Sometimes he became very lonely.

One day, he thought of a way he might get people to visit him.

He shouted, "Help, help. A wolf is coming to eat the sheep."

Everyone ran from the village to help him save the sheep.

Of course there was no wolf there.

The shepherd boy had just been pretending.

A few days later he became lonely again.

He shouted, "Help, help. A wolf is coming to eat the sheep."

Everyone ran from the village again.

When they saw that he was pretending again everyone was angry.

The next day, a wolf did come to eat the sheep.

The boy screamed for help again but this time the people in the village just laughed, and the wolf ate all the sheep.

Moral: A liar will not be believed even if he speaks the truth.

Questions:

What did the boy do everyday?

Where did he watch the sheep?

Why do you think he became lonely?

What did he do to get people to visit him?

What happened the first and second times he screamed for help?

How did the people from the village feel about his pretending?

Why did he shout for help the third time?

What did the people do then?

What happened when no one came to help?

What is the moral of the story?

ACTIVITY IV CHECKER SHUFFLE BOARD

Material: Checkers for each child with his name on them. Large sheet of glossy construction paper marked off in two equal halves. One half serves as a runway and the other is further divided into nine equal squares numbered one through nine.

Procedure: When the children answer their problems correctly they are allowed to snap their checkers from the runway to the squares. The first to reach a score of twenty makes up questions for the others to lip read. Advise the class that it is permissible to knock the other children's checkers from the board with their checkers. Only one checker is snapped for each answer.

Sentences:

	legs		man
	arms		horse
	feet		cow
How many	eyes	has a	chicken
	toes		sheep
	ears		goat
	fingers		pig

LESSON NINE

ACTIVITY I WHAT HOLIDAY IS IT?

Material: Cue words to be used: New Year's Day, Lincoln's Birthday, Valentine's Day, April Fool's Day, Halloween, Thanksgiving, Christmas, Fourth of July.

Procedure: The children are called upon individually to answer the riddle with the name of the holiday. Repeat and re-phrase as much as necessary but do not continue until the child called on answers correctly.

Sentences:

This is a very important day because it starts our year.

We go to parties on this day and stay up very late.

What holiday is it?

Answer: New Year's Day.

This is the birthday of a famous president.
This man freed the slaves in the South.
What holiday is it?

Answer: Lincoln's birthday.

We see hearts and cupids on this holiday.
We send presents to our girl friends and boy friends.
What holiday is it?

Answer: Valentine's Day.

This holiday comes in April.
We play tricks on our friends on this day.
What holiday is it?

Answer: April Fool's Day.

This is the holiday when we wear costumes and masks.

We go to people's doors and ask for candy.

What holiday is it?

Answer: Halloween.

This is the day on which the Pilgrims had dinner with the Indians.

We eat turkey and pumpkin pie on this holiday.

What holiday is it?

Answer: Thanksgiving.

We all get presents and give presents on this holiday.

There is snow on the ground and it is cold.

What holiday is it?

Answer: Christmas.

The Declaration of Independence was signed on this day.

We shoot fireworks and play with cap pistols on this day.

What holiday is it?

Answer: Fourth of July.

ACTIVITY II   WHOSE BIRTHDAY IS IT?

See Lesson Three, Activity II, Intermediate, for material and procedure. Draw picture of an axe and a cherry tree.

Sentences:

This holiday comes in February.

It celebrates someone's birthday.

This man was a famous soldier.

He was also famous for something else.

His wife's name was Martha.

He was sometimes called the Father of our Country.

He chopped down a cherry tree when he was young.

His father did not punish him because he told the truth.

His first name is George.

A city and a state have been named after him.

Answer: George Washington.

ACTIVITY III

THE GOOSE WITH THE GOLDEN EGGS

Cue words: different, money, greedy, killed.

Sentences:

Once a very poor man was walking through the forest.

He was sad because he had no money to buy food.

He said he would be happy if he had just a little money to buy a piece of bread.

While he was walking, he saw a goose under some bushes.

He was going to kill it for food but he found out that it was a very different kind of goose.

It laid one golden egg every day!

The man was very happy at first.

He sold the golden eggs each day and had plenty of food.

He bought a house and then a farm with the money.

After some time passed he became less happy.

This man had a bigger farm and that man had a better house.

So he killed the goose and opened it to get all the golden eggs at once.

But there were no eggs inside.

Moral: Be happy with what you have.

Questions:

Where was the man walking?

Why was he so unhappy?

What did he find under a bush?

Why was this goose different?

How many eggs did the man get from the goose?

What did he buy with the money?

Why did he become unhappy?

What did he do to get more eggs?

What did he find when he opened the goose?

What is the moral of the story?

ACTIVITY IV STEP FORWARD PLEASE

Cue words: George Washington, Abraham Lincoln, St. Valentine, Santa Claus, Hans Christian Andersen, Superman, Franklin Roosevelt, Eisenhower, Mickey Mouse, Thomas Jefferson, and well known figures in your community such as the Mayor, Police Chief, etc.

See Lesson Four, Activity IV, Intermediate, for procedure.

Sentences:

I am a famous person whose name is ....

LESSON TEN

ACTIVITY I COMMON EXPRESSIONS

Material: Blackboard and chalk for the following common expressions:

1. A stitch in time saves nine.
2. Look before you leap.
3. Haste makes waste.
4. A bird in the hand is worth two in the bush.
5. An apple a day keeps the doctor away.
6. Moss never grows on a rolling stone.
7. Look for the silver lining.

Procedure: Go through each of these expressions aloud explaining the significance; then go through them a second time without voice. Then, give the sentences below individually and have the child called on write the sentence next to its counterpart on the board.

Sentences:

Don't always think that you'll be unhappy.

Answer: Look for the silver lining.

If you eat the right food, you won't get sick.

Answer: An apple a day keeps the doctor away.

You should think about something before doing it.

Answer: Look before you leap.

You can often lose time by hurrying.

Answer: Haste makes waste.

If you keep busy, you keep happy.

Answer: Moss never grows on a rolling stone.

Be happy with what you have; don't worry about what you might get.

Answer: A bird in the hand is worth two in the bush.

Sometimes a little work done early saves a lot of work later.

Answer: A stitch in time saves nine.

ACTIVITY II WHICH EXPRESSION IS IT?

Material: Paper and crayons for each child.

Procedure: The class draws the action and objects described by the teacher. When they have completed the sketch, they are to write the title, a familiar expression from Activity I, above the sketch.

Sentences:
Draw a tall mountain.
Now draw a man standing on the top of it.
Put a blindfold over his eyes.
Which expression is it?

Answer: Look before you leap.

Draw a picture of a big lady standing up.
She's wearing a dress that's too tight.
The side is popping open.
Which expression is it?

Answer: A stitch in time saves nine.

Draw a picture of a bus.
Now draw a man running to catch it.
Draw a big hole in front of him.
Which expression is it?

Answer: Haste makes waste.

Draw a picture of a man with a white coat.
Put a cage around the man.
Draw a picture of a boy eating an apple.

Which expression is it?

Answer: An apple a day keeps the doctor away.

ACTIVITY III THE FROG AND THE OX

Cue words: Father, excited, monster, mountain, horns, legs, ox, taller, wide, puffed, burst, pieces.

Sentences:

One day, a little frog ran home to his father.

He was so excited, he couldn't speak at first.

"I have just seen a terrible monster. It was as big as a mountain and had long horns."

Father frog said, "That was the farmer's ox you saw.

He may be a little taller than I am but I can make myself as wide."

So the father frog puffed himself up and asked, "Was he as big as this?"

"He was much bigger" the little frog said.

The father frog puffed and puffed again.

"Was he as big as that" he asked.

"No father, he was much bigger than that."

The father frog puffed and puffed and puffed until he was very wide.

When he tried to talk again, he opened his mouth and burst into pieces.

Moral: Don't try to be something that you're not.

Questions:

To whom did the little frog run?

What did he think he had seen?

What did his father tell him he had seen?

Was the Father frog as tall as the ox?

Was the father frog as wide as the ox?

How did the Father frog make himself bigger?

What happened when he puffed and puffed?

Do you think he could ever have made himself as big as the ox?

What is the moral of the story?

ACTIVITY IV   TELEPHONE CONVERSATION

Material: Toy telephones for each child.

Procedure: Have the children pair off to hold telephone conversations choosing any of the following topics: baseball, cooking, dancing, movies, dating, school. Instruct them to use expressions which one ordinarily hears about their topic. See which of the pairs can hold the longest lip reading conversation without stopping.

LESSON ELEVEN

ACTIVITY I   ANIMAL FOOD

Material: Large slot chart, pictures mounted on construction paper of the following: mouse, cow, man, dog, rabbit, fish, seal, chicken, cat, horse, cheese, hay, steak, bones, carrots, worms, fish, grain, mouse, cat. No cue words are given.

Procedure: Place the pictures of the animals in one column on the chart and the food pictures on a table. As you read the sentences have the children match the food to the proper animal.

Sentences:

I am a small animal; I have a long tail and live in a house or in a barn.
I eat cheese and I hate cats.

Answer: Mouse and cheese.

I live in the water and like to eat fish.
I balance balls on my nose at the zoo.
I have fins but I am not a fish.

Answer: Seal and fish.

I am the animal you think of at Easter.
I have long ears and a short, round tail.
I like to eat carrots.

Answer: Rabbit and carrots.

I live in the water and like to swim.
Men try to catch me with hooks.
They put worms on the hooks for me to eat

Answer: Fish and worms.

I live on a farm.
I have a long tail and horns on my head.
I give milk and eat hay.

Answer: Cow and hay.

I live in the city where I work and play.
I have two arms and two legs.
I like to eat steak.

Answer: Man and steak.

I am a small, furry animal.
People keep me in the house.
I catch mice in the house and eat them.

Answer: Cat and mouse.

I am a large animal that lives on a farm.
I can pull a plow or carry people on my back.
I eat the grass in the pasture.

Answer: Horse and grass.

I am man's best friend.
He keeps me in his house and on his farm.
He feeds me bones so I will chase cats away.

Answer: Dog and bones.

I live on a farm where I lay eggs.
The farmer feeds me grain to eat.
When I stop laying eggs, the farmer eats me.

Answer: Chicken and grain.

ACTIVITY II A TRIP TO THE FARM

Material: None.

Procedure: This is a creative dramatics situation in which the various children are assigned

the roles of Grandfather, Grandmother, grand-
children. The children are spending the day on
their Grandfather's farm where they will do the
chores, feed the animals and eat dinner.

ACTIVITY III   THE WIND AND THE SUN

Cue words: North Wind, cold, gentle, grabbed,
warm rays.

Sentences:

One day the North Wind and the Sun met
in the sky.

The North Wind was very strong and cold.

The Sun was warm and gentle.

The North Wind bragged, "I am much
stronger than you. I can do anything better than
you."

The Sun said, "Just because you can blow
harder than I can doesn't mean you are better."

The North Wind said, "I can prove I'm better than you.

Do you see that man down there walking
along the road?

Let's see who can get his coat off first."

The North Wind blew a strong cold wind at
the man and almost blew his coat away.

The man grabbed his coat and pulled it tight
to keep the wind away.

Then the sun let his warm rays fall on the
man.

The man smiled up at the kind sun and took
off his coat.

He would not need it on such a fine, warm day.

Moral: We win many things with kindness that cannot be won with force.

Questions:

Where did the North Wind and the Sun meet?

What did the North Wind say?

What did the Sun tell the North Wind?

How did the North Wind try to prove he was better than the Sun?

What did the man do when the wind blew?

What did the man do when the sun made him warm?

What is the moral of the story?

ACTIVITY IV   ANIMAL DARTS

Material: Suction tip darts, pictures on animals and food used in Activity I. (scotch-tape to board.)

Procedure: See Lesson Three, Activity IV, Intermediate.

Sentences: Throw the dart at the ....

LESSON TWELVE

ACTIVITY I   WHAT SHOULD I WEAR?

Material: Pictures of the following articles of clothing mounted on construction paper:

swimming suit, snow suit, fancy bonnet, corduroy pants, rain coat, overalls, party dress, shorts. Use pictures for cue words.

Procedure: As the children answer the statements with the name of the article of clothing, they are given the picture of that item to hold for the next activity. The children are called on individually.

Sentences:

I am going to the beach today.
I will wear this to go in the water.
What should I wear?

Answer: swimming suit.

It is snowing outside today.
I want to go out to play in the snow.
What should I wear?

Answer: snow suit.

I go to church with my family.
I wear something on my head that goes with my dress.
What should I wear?

Answer: fancy bonnet.

This is winter and I am going to school.
The other boys wear these, too.
What should I wear?

Answer: corduroy pants.

It is raining outside today.
I want to go for a walk in the rain.
What should I wear?

Answer: rain coat.

My grandfather has a farm in the country.
I want to go there to work today.
What should I wear?

Answer: overalls.

My girl friend is having a birthday party.
She has invited all the girls to it.
What should I wear?

Answer: party dress.

This is a nice, warm day in Summer.
I want to play outside in the yard.
What should I wear?

Answer: shorts.

ACTIVITY II CLEANING THE CLOSET

Material: Pictures of clothing retained from
the previous activity; boxes labeled Cleaners,
Closet, and Laundry.

Procedure: As the sentence is read, the child
with the article of clothing mentioned puts it
in the right box.

Sentences:

Mother needs more room in the closet.

She wants you to put away the clothes we don't need.

Let's give the snow suit to the cleaners.

Put the party dress in the laundry basket.

The fancy bonnet is dirty and has to go to the cleaners.

Let's leave the rain coat in the closet because it might rain tomorrow.

The overalls need to be washed so let's put them in the laundry basket.

The shorts can stay in the closet because they don't take up much room.

The corduroy pants are too dirty to be washed so let's send them to the cleaners.

ACTIVITY III

THE LARK AND HER BABIES

Cue words: wheat, hatched, neighbors, worry, seldom, relatives, usually.

Sentences:

A lark had made her nest in a field of wheat.

When her eggs hatched she would fly away each day to find food.

She told her babies to listen carefully to everything they heard while she was gone.

One day they heard the farmer talking to his son.

He told the son to ask their friends and neighbors to come help cut the wheat.

The mother lark told her babies not to worry.

"Neighbors and friends seldom rush to help
each other," she said.

The next day the farmer sent his son to ask
the relatives to help cut the wheat.

The mother lark told her babies not to worry
yet.

"Relatives are in no hurry to help each other,"
she said.

The next day the farmer told his son that they
would cut the wheat themselves.

When the babies told the mother lark this,
she got ready to leave.

"When a man plans to do his own work, it
usually gets done," she said.

Moral: Don't wait for others to do your work
because it might not get done.

Questions:

Where did the lark make her nest?

Why did she leave each day?

What did she ask the baby larks to do?

Whom did the farmer want to help the first
time?

Whom did he ask to help the second time?

Why didn't the lark worry when the farmer
asked the neighbors and relatives to help?

Why did the lark finally decide to leave?

What is the moral of the story?

ACTIVITY IV FISHING FOR CLOTHES

Material: Attach paper clips to the pictures from the activities in the beginning of this lesson; a magnet is attached to the string.

Procedure: See Lesson Two, Activity IV, Intermediate.

LESSON THIRTEEN

ACTIVITY I WHERE AM I?

Material: Cue words to be used: school, farm, beach, mountains, church, store, kitchen, living room, movie, circus.

Procedure: The children are called on individually to answer the riddles. Repeat or rephrase as much as necessary.

Sentences:

I am in a room with many other children.
I can see blackboards, maps, pictures and desks.

Where am I?

Answer: school.

I am out in the country.
I can see animals, corn, wheat and a barn.
Where am I?

Answer: farm.

I am near a lot of water.
I can see rubber balls, people swimming, and
a lot of sand.
Where am I?

Answer: beach.

I am in a beautiful building.
I come here every Sunday to pray.
Where am I?

Answer: church.

I am in a very big building.
I see tomatoes, potatoes, corn, and cookies.
Where am I?

Answer: store.

I am in my own home.
I am watching mother make dinner.
Where am I?

Answer: kitchen.

I am in my home again.
I am sitting in a chair watching television.
Where am I?

Answer: living room.

I am in a very dark place with many others.
All the people are watching a large screen.
Where am I?

Answer: movie.

I am in a bright, noisy place.

I can see clowns and animals here.
Where am I?

Answer: circus.

ACTIVITY II

WHERE WOULD YOU PUT IT?

Material: Blackboard and chalk. No cue
words are given.

Procedure: Draw four columns on the board
and label them Home, Farm, Circus and School.
Four of the children are selected to be in charge
of one column each. The child writes the name
of the object in his column if it belongs there.
If he makes a mistake, his place is taken by one
of the waiting children. Repeat the sentence
only once.

Sentences: Where would you put a ....?

Items: (given out of order)
bed, stove, toothbrush, refrigerator, mother.
Answer: home.

cow, plow, farmer, barnyard, chickens.
Answer: farm.

bear, monkey, trapeze, acrobat, elephant.
Answer: circus.

ruler, teacher, blackboard, library, chalk.
Answer: school.

ACTIVITY III

THE COUNTRY MOUSE AND THE CITY MOUSE

Cue words: field, invited, visit, arrived, corn, wheat, poorly, enter, honey, rich, frightened, crackers, hole, sneaked, decided.

Sentences:

Once there was a mouse who lived in the country.

He invited his friend the city mouse to come visit him.

The city mouse arrived the next day.

As soon as the city mouse arrived, they sat down to eat.

They had a dinner of plain corn and wheat.

After the meal, the city mouse invited his friend to visit him in the city.

"Mice do not live so poorly in the city," he said.

When they arrived at the home of the city mouse, they sneaked in.

"Be very quiet or the cat might hear us," the city mouse said.

They went into the kitchen of the city mouse and sat down to eat.

They ate cheese, fruit and honey.

The country mouse thought his friend was very rich.

As they were eating, a man opened the door.

They were frightened and ran into a hole in the wall.

When the man left, they came out to eat some fine crackers.

Then a woman came into the kitchen.

They ran to hide in the hole again.

Both the mice were very frightened.

"This happens all the time but you get used to it," the city mouse said.

The country mouse decided to leave right away.

He sneaked past the woman and the man.

He walked on his toes past the cat.

When he got back to the country he said he would never leave again.

Questions:

Where did the country mouse live?

Whom did he invite for a visit?

What did they have for dinner?

Where did they go after the meal?

Did they eat a good meal in the city?

Who came in while they were eating?

Why did the country mouse leave so soon?

What do you think the moral of the story should be?

ACTIVITY IV   WHERE DID I HIDE IT?

Material: Objects carried or worn by the children, and objects around the room.

Procedure: Each child has at least one turn to hide some object while all the others close their eyes. Then he describes and names the object to the class and gives directions to find it. The one who does so then hides another object to be found.

LESSON FOURTEEN

ACTIVITY I

IN WHAT ROOM WILL I FIND IT?

Material: Doll house and the following doll furniture: stove, bed, closet, sink, bathtub, food, television set, cookies, shoes, lamp, handkerchief.

Procedure: The children are called on individually to name the object described and having done so are allowed to place the object in the appropriate room of the doll house.

Sentences:

This is large and white; Mother cooks on it. What is it and where will I find it?

Answer: stove and kitchen.

I am sleepy and want to lie down in this. What is it and where will I find it?

Answer: bed and bedroom.

My dress is dirty and I need a fresh one. What is it and where will I find it?

Answer: dress and bedroom closet.

My hands are dirty and I need something in which I can wash them.
What is it and where will I find it?

Answer: sink and bathroom.

I fell in the mud and have to take a bath.
What do I need and where will I find it?

Answer: bathtub and bathroom.

I am at home and want to watch cowboys fight.
What do I need and where will I find it?

Answer: television set and living room.

I have finished lunch and want something sweet.
What do I need and where will I find it?

Answer: cookies and kitchen.

I want to play outside and have to wear something on my feet.
What do I need and where will I find it?

Answer: shoes and bedroom.

I want to read but it is too dark.
What do I need and where will I find it?

Answer: lamp and living room.

I have a cold and my nose is running.
What do I need and where will I find it?

Answer: handkerchief and bedroom dresser.

ACTIVITY II WHERE DOES IT BELONG?

Material: Blackboard and chalk. No cue words are given.

Procedure: Draw four columns on the board and label them Kitchen, Living Room, Bedroom and Bathroom. Four of the children are selected to be in charge of one column each. The child writes the name of the object in his column if it belongs there. If he makes a mistake his place is taken by one of the waiting children. Repeat the sentence only once.

Sentences: Where would you put a ....?

Items: (given out of order)
stove, refrigerator, ham, fork, frying pan.

Answer: kitchen.

television set, arm chair, couch, coffee table, ash tray.

Answer: living room.

pillow, mattress, sheet, bed, dressing table.

Answer: bedroom.

bar of soap, towel, bathtub, washcloth, shower.

Answer: bathroom.

ACTIVITY III THE LION AND THE MOUSE

Cue words: forest, back, paw, woke, begged, mercy, favor, small, joke, hunters, tied, gnawed, important.

Sentences:

One hot day a lion was sleeping in the forest.

A mouse walked by and thought it would be fun to play on the lion.

He began by running up and down the lion's back.

This was so much fun he decided to run up and down the lion's paws.

This woke the lion up, however.

He grabbed the mouse and held him to his mouth.

The lion opened his mouth very wide to eat the little mouse.

The frightened mouse begged for mercy.

"Please let me go and some day I will return the favor."

The lion laughed and laughed.

He thought it was funny that a little mouse could ever help him.

He was so big that all of the small animals asked him for favors.

He was pleased by the joke so he let the mouse go free.

A few days later, some hunters caught the lion in a trap.

They tied him to a tree and went to catch some more animals.

The lion roared as he tried to get free but he couldn't get loose.

The little mouse heard the lion roaring and came to see what was the matter.

He ran to the lion and gnawed through the ropes.

They both ran away before the hunters could return.

Moral: It is important to be kind to everyone, even little friends.

Questions:

What was the lion doing in the forest?
Who saw him sleeping in the forest?
What did the mouse do?
What did the lion do when he woke?
Why didn't he eat the mouse?
What happened to the lion later?
What did the mouse do?
What is the moral of the story?

ACTIVITY IV CHECKER TOSS

Material: Doll house from Activity II, one checker for each child. Cue words: bedroom, kitchen, bathroom, living room.

Procedure: Each child is called on in turn to toss his checker to the room named in the sentence. If he lands in the correct room he scores one point. The first to reach a score of five points gets to call the directions for the others.

Sentences:

Toss the checker in the
{
bedroom
kitchen
living room
bathroom
}

LESSON FIFTEEN

ACTIVITY I WEATHER MAP

Material: Large map of the United States and the following word labels on stick pins: warm, hot, pleasant, cool, cold, humid, rainy, snow, windy, shine.

Procedure: After going through the labels as cue words, pin them in a column on the margin of the map. As the children repeat the sentences correctly, they take the proper label and stick it in the state that was named. (It should not be necessary to give the names of the states as cue words at this time since this will be done in Lesson Seventeen, Activity II. Briefly, go through the following states without voice pointing to them on the map: Pennsylvania, New York, Vermont, Missouri, Wyoming, Montana, North Dakota, Washington, Mississippi, Louisiana.)

Sentences:

It seems quite warm in Pennsylvania today.
New York is very hot for this time of year.
Vermont is expecting a great deal of rain.
In Missouri, the weather is very pleasant.
Parts of Wyoming are very cold today.
North Dakota has had snow all day.
Washington will be windy for a week.
In Mississippi the sun is shining brightly.
Louisiana is very humid as usual.
Montana is expecting a cold wave.

ACTIVITY II More Weather

Material: Name plates with Warm & Pleasant, Rain, Snow, Hot. Cue words: warm and pleasant, rain, snow, hot, North, South, East, West.

Procedure: Each child is given a nameplate with a particular weather condition on it. The teacher pretends to be a weather announcer on a television program. As a weather condition somewhere in the country is announced, the child wearing that name card must rise quickly and then sit down. This activity is done quickly with only one statement of the sentence.

Sentences:

The weather across the country is quite strange.

So many things are happening in the North, the East, the South and the West.

In the East there is a great deal of rain.

In the West it is very hot.

In the North it is cold and there is snow.

In the South it is warm and pleasant.

But the weather is changing quickly.

Tomorrow it will be hot in the South.

It will be warm in the East.

We expect snow all over the west.

And the rain is going to fall in the North.

The weather looks strange for the weekend.

There will be rain and snow in the West.

There will be warm, pleasant weather in the morning and hot weather in the afternoon.

And Sunday, the whole country will be hot, rainy, cold and warm at the same time.

ACTIVITY III

THE TRAVELERS AND THE BEAR

Cue words: trip, promised, danger, huge, pretended, dead, smelled, harm, safe, whisper, judge.

Sentences:

Two men were going on a trip to a small village.

They had to walk through a forest on their trip.

They each promised to help the other if there were any danger.

A little while after they entered the forest, they heard a loud noise.

It was a huge bear and he was coming right at them.

One of the men quickly ran up a tree and hid.

The other was slower and could not climb trees.

He fell to the ground and pretended to be dead.

He had heard that bears would not eat dead men.

The bear came up and smelled his head.

Then the bear went away without harming him.

The man who had hidden in the tree ran to his friend on the ground.

He tried to joke with his friend so he would not be angry that he had run away.

He said, "I'm glad you're safe.

What did that old bear whisper in your ear?"

The man on the ground said, "He told me to judge a man by what he does, not what he says he will do."

Questions:

Where were the men going?

What did each promise to do?

What did they hear in the forest?

What did the two men do?

Did the man who ran up the tree do what he had promised to do?

Why did the bear go away?

What did the man who ran up the tree ask his friend?

Why did the man who ran up the tree pretend that the bear had whispered something?

What is the moral of the story?

ACTIVITY IV DARTS

Material: Suction tip darts; weather map with the various stick pin labels still in place from Activity I.

Procedure: Call on the children individually to throw the darts at specific weather labels. If they hit the label they score four points; if they miss the label but hit the state containing the label, they score three points; if they hit an adjacent state, they score two points; if they are two states away, they score one point. The first to reach a score of ten points calls the directions for the others.

Sentences:

Throw the dart somewhere ⎱ warm
hot
pleasant
cool
cold
humid
rainy
snowy
windy
shiny

LESSON SIXTEEN

ACTIVITY I   LET'S GO TO THE FAIR

Material: Blackboard and chalk. Cue words: cotton candy, bingo, ferris wheel, merry-go-round, balloons, pin the tail on the donkey, hot dogs, soda pop, rifles, bottles, rides, penny arcade, animals, judging contest, parade, march, horses, bumper cars, games.

Procedure: Draw a very large tent cover at the top of the blackboard. The children are called on individually to draw the action described in the sentences.

Sentences:

Let's go to the fair and eat cotton candy and play bingo.

Let's go to the fair and ride the ferris wheel and the merry-go-round.

Let's go to the fair and break the balloons and pin the tail on the donkey.

Let's go to the fair and eat hot dogs and drink soda pop.

Let's go to the fair and shoot the rifles and break the targets made out of bottles.

Let's go to the fair and go on all the rides and play in the penny arcade.

Let's go to the fair and look at the animals and watch the judging contest.

Let's go to the fair and see the parade and march along beside it.

Let's go to the fair and ride the horses and the bumper cars.

Let's go to the fair and play all the games and see how much we can win.

ACTIVITY II WHAT Is IT?

Material: Blackboard and chalk.

Procedure: Underline eleven blanks in a horizontal row on the board and inform the class that you are going to spell something they would see at the fair. Each time they lip read a sentence in the story they may guess just one letter. Spell the word *Ferris Wheel*.

Sentences:

Mother and Father took us to the fair.

We ate candy, hot dogs, pop corn and drank soda pop.

When we finished eating we went on many rides.

We went on the bumper cars and the horses.

We rode on the merry-go-round until we were dizzy.

After the rides, we watched the parade.

There were donkeys in the parade and funny animals too.

We saw clowns and trained dogs.

We had a good time at the fair but we became tired.

We left the fair grounds when our money was gone.

We went home and fell asleep before dinner.

We weren't very hungry for some reason.

ACTIVITY III

THE DOG AND HIS REFLECTION

Cue words: greedy, master, stole, butcher, bridge, reflection.

Sentences:

Once there was a very greedy dog.

He never thought that he had enough to eat.

His master would always feed him but he was still hungry.

One day he stole a piece of meat from the butcher.

On his way home he had to cross a bridge which was over a stream.

He looked over the side of the bridge and saw his reflection in the water.

Since he wasn't very smart, he thought it was another dog with a piece of meat.

Since he was greedy, he snapped at his reflection to get the other piece of meat.

Of course when he did this, he dropped the real piece of meat.

Moral: Don't try too hard to get things you imagine you need; you may lose the things you really have.

Questions:

Did the dog's master give him enough food?
Where did the dog get some extra food?
Why was he crossing a bridge?
What did he see over the side of the bridge?
What did he *think* he saw over the side?
What did he do when he saw his reflection?
What happened when he snapped at his reflection?
What is the moral of the story?

ACTIVITY IV

PIN THE TAIL ON THE DONKEY

Material: Cork board, several balloons, donkey's tail with a large pin in it and the following pictures: clown, hot dog, rifle, ferris wheel, pie, soda pop.

Procedure: Pin the pictures of the circus items and the filled balloons on the board in random order but do not pin the donkey on the board yet. Choose a child to pin the tail on the donkey and have him look at the board to become familiar with the placement of the pictures. Then turn him around so he faces the class but has his back to the board and give him the donkey tail which he holds above his head. He is to try to pin the tail on the donkey before popping the ballon following the directions of the class.

Sentences:

$$\left.\begin{array}{l}\text{right} \\ \text{middle} \\ \text{left}\end{array}\right\}$$ of the *hot dog*.

Move to the middle {of the *hot dog*.

USE OF VOICE

The remaining lessons in the *Intermediate Lessons* section of this book are to be given using a soft voice in order to allow the children to synthesize both visual and auditory clues. As has already been stated in the *Primary Lessons* Section, in the note on the use of voice preceding Lesson Twenty, this will insure that the child employs optimally those skills in lip reading which he has developed in a rigorous, voiceless, learning situation.

LESSON SEVENTEEN

ACTIVITY I LET'S TAKE A VACATION

Material: Large map of the United States and paper cut-outs of the following items: mountain, fish, cheese, magnolias, horses, corn, boat, skis, baseball glove, hula dancers, bed. Pins should be stuck through these cut-outs. Cue words: Use the pictures for cue words and the map for the names of the fifty states.

Procedure: The child called on repeats the sentence and then goes to the map to complete the action of that sentence by placing the cut-outs in the proper state.

Sentences:

If we go to Pennsylvania, we can ride in the mountains.

If we go to Minnesota, we can all go fishing in the lakes.

If we go to Hawaii, we can see the hula dancers on the beach.

If we go to New York, we can see the baseball games.

If we go to Wisconsin, we can eat some fine cheese.

If we go to Louisiana, we can see the magnolias.

If we go to Texas, we can ride the horses.

If we go to Mississippi, we can have fun on the boats.

If we go to Illinois we can see fields of corn.

If we stay home in (own state) we can relax in bed.

ACTIVITY II A Cross Country Trip

Material: Map of the United States used in previous activity and paper cut-outs of the following items: car, boat, train, covered wagon, plane, shoes, bicycle, horse. Pins are to be used with these items. Cue words: cut-out items, fifty states, North, South, East, West.

Procedure: See Activity I of this lesson.

Sentences:

We left home in our car and went west to California.

We left our car in California and took a boat to Hawaii.

We took the boat to Texas where we rented some horses.

We returned the horses and took a covered wagon north to the border.

We got on a train and rode through Louisiana, Mississippi and Arkansas.

We got off the train in Arkansas and took a plane to New York City.

We left the plane in New York City and walked until our shoes were worn out.

We rented some bicycles and peddled through Maine, New Hampshire and Vermont.

ACTIVITY III

THE FROGS WHO WANTED A KING

Cue words: pool, forest, mosquitoes, missing, leader, lion, log, floated, complained, angry, bothered, roared, stork.

Sentences:

Many frogs lived happily together in a pool in the forest.

They played and danced and ate mosquitoes all day.

One or two of the frogs felt that something was missing.

They said, "It's not right for frogs just to dance and play and eat mosquitoes all day."

They felt that frogs should do something better with their time.

The other frogs said, "But we have no leader to tell us what to do."

So all the frogs went to the king of the forest who was the lion and asked for a leader.

He laughed and said, "Go home and I will send you a king for the frogs."

The next day the lion went to the pool.

He threw a log into the water and said, "This is your new king."

The silly frogs waited for their new king to help them but of course the log just floated in the water.

The frogs complained to the lion, "Our new king just floats in the water all day.

He doesn't really lead us at all."

The lion was angry.

He didn't like being bothered by the frogs.

"Go home," he roared, "I will send you another leader!"

The next day he sent a stork who ate up all the little frogs in the pool.

Moral: When you're happy don't look for ways to be sad.

Questions:

Where did the frogs live?

What did they do all day?

Do you think most of the frogs were happy?

What did the frogs ask the lion to give them?

What did the lion give them the first time?

Why weren't they happy with the log?

Was the lion pleased when they came back?

What did he send them the second time?

What did the stork do to the frogs?

What is the moral of the story?

ACTIVITY IV   I TOOK A TRIP

Material: None.

Procedure: The children are seated in a circle so all faces can be seen easily. The first child names a state through which he took a trip; the second child names that state and adds another. The children continue adding states until one makes a mistake. This child is eliminated and

the others start over again continuing until there
is only one of the group remaining.

Sentences:

    I took a trip through ....

    I took a trip through ...., ..., ..., and .....

LESSON EIGHTEEN

ACTIVITY I   LET'S GO TO THE SYMPHONY

Material: Phonograph and recording of the
instruments of the symphony if available; cork
board and the following name cards: Wood-
wind, Wind, Percussion, String; pictures of the
following instruments: clarinet, trumpet, violin,
drum, trombone, flute, piano, saxophone, cymbal, bass fiddle, oboe, tuba, french horn, bassoon,
xylophone.   Use the pictures and name cards
for cue words.

Procedure: Make four columns on the bulletin
board and label each with one of the name cards.
The child who is called on repeats the sentence
and places the picture of the instrument named
in the correct column.

Sentences:

    The .... is a member of the ....
family.

    clarinet, saxophone, oboe, bassoon, flute.

    Answer: Woodwind.

trumpet, trombone, tuba, french horn.
Answer: Wind.

violin, bass fiddle.
Answer: String.

piano, cymbal, drum, xylophone.
Answer: Percussion.

ACTIVITY II WHAT INSTRUMENT IS IT?

Material: Cork board and pictures of instruments from the previous activity. Cue words: wood, silver keys, reed, mouthpiece, finished (painted or plated), gold lacquer, skin, strings, catgut, horse hair bow, brass, tube, ivory, eighty-eight, body, musician, symphony.

Procedure: When the child who is called on recognizes the instrument being described, he places the picture of it on the board.

Sentences:

This instrument is made of dark wood. It has silver keys and is as long as a man's arm. It is played with a reed held in the mouthpiece.

What instrument is it?

Answer: clarinet.

This instrument is made of brass. It is finished in gold lacquer and has only three keys. It is played by blowing into a mouthpiece shaped like a cup. It's two feet long.

What instrument is it?

Answer: trumpet.

This instrument is made of wood and is covered with an animal's skin. It is played by beating the skin with wooden sticks. Some of these are very big while others are small.

What instrument is it?

Answer: drum.

This instrument is made of wood and has strings made of catgut. It is played by bringing the horsehair bow across the strings. There are keys to tighten the strings at one end of the instrument.

What instrument is it?

Answer: violin.

This instrument is made of brass and is finished with gold lacquer. It has no keys but it does have a long tube. The tube slides in and out. It is played by blowing into a cup-shaped mouthpiece.

What instrument is it?

Answer: trombone.

This instrument is the biggest one there is. It is made of wood and ivory. It has eighty-

eight keys which are black and white. It is
played by striking the keys with all the fingers.
What instrument is it?

Answer: piano.

This instrument is made of brass and is finished in gold lacquer. It has many keys along
its body. It is played by blowing a reed held in
its mouthpiece.
What instrument is it?

Answer: saxophone.

This instrument may be made of wood or silver. It is not held in front of the musician but
to the side. It is played by blowing into a small
hole at one end. This is the smallest instrument
in the symphony.
What instrument is it?

Answer: flute.

ACTIVITY III   THE WOODMAN'S LOST AXE

Cue words: bank (of a river), accidentally,
earn a living, fairy, surface, silver, golden, honest, greedy, angry, chopping.

Sentences:

A woodman was chopping trees along the
bank of a river.

His axe slipped out of his hand accidentally
and fell into the water.

He sat down and cried because he could not earn a living without his axe.

A fairy who lived in the water swam to the surface and asked him what was wrong.

When the fairy heard what had happened, he dived below the surface and swam up with a silver axe in his hand.

When the woodman told the fairy that it was not his, the fairy smiled.

The fairy dived again and came up with a golden axe this time.

The woodman said that this was not his axe either.

The fine fairy was so pleased with the honest woodman that he gave him the gold and silver axes as well as his own.

The woodsman ran to tell his friends the wonderful news and show the axes.

One greedy man who heard the story ran back to the river as fast as he could.

He threw his axe into the water and sat down and cried very loudly.

When the fairy swam to the surface the greedy man lied that he had lost his axe.

As soon as the fairy swam to the surface with the golden axe, the greedy man claimed it was his.

The fairy was very angry that the man had lied to him.

The fairy not only kept the golden axe but kept the greedy man's axe as well.

Moral: Honesty is the best policy.

Questions:

How did the woodsman lose his axe?

What kind of an axe do you think it was?

What did the fairy bring to the surface the first time?

What did the fairy bring the second time?

What did the fairy do to reward the woodsman's honesty?

What did the greedy man do?

How did the fairy reward him for lying?

What is the moral of the story?

ACTIVITY IV   THE SYMPHONY PLAYS

Material: The following word pairs are written on the board: flute-*whistles,* drum-*booms,* violin-*hums,* cymbal-*claps,* trumpet-*holds nose and hums.*

Procedure: Each child chooses one of the imaginary instruments listed on the board which he must then play in the manner indicated by its word pair. A familiar tune, such as "My Country 'Tis of Thee" or "Old MacDonald Had a Farm" is hummed, whistled, clapped, etc. by the group even during the changes called for by the teacher. Periodically, the teacher will ask members of the class to exchange instrument roles while they are "playing."

Sentences:

Johnny be the { trumpet
drum
flute
violin
cymbal } and *Bob* be the drum.

LESSON NINETEEN

ACTIVITY I LET'S GO TO THE DANCE

Material: Magazine picture of a high school or junior high school prom. Cue words: suits, formals, carnations, corsages, high heels, orchestra, bandstand, uncomfortable, bashful, cutting in, saxophone, trumpet, "Goodnight Sweetheart," small talk.

Procedure: The children are called on individually to repeat the sentences about things they might *see* or *hear* at a prom.

Sentences:

What might you see at a dance?

You might see boys wearing suits dancing with girls wearing formals.

You might see tall boys dancing with short girls.

You might see boys wearing carnations in their button-holes and girls carrying corsages.

You might see boys with big shiny shoes stepping on the girls' feet in high heels.

You might see an orchestra on a bandstand.

What might you hear at a dance?

You might hear uncomfortable girls trying to make small talk with bashful boys.

You might hear one boy cutting in on another to dance with a girl.

You might hear a saxophone trying to play louder than a trumpet.

You might hear a boy asking a girl to have a dance with him.

You might hear the orchestra playing "Goodnight Sweetheart" when it's time to leave.

ACTIVITY II

THE FARMER, HIS SON AND THE DONKEY

Cue words: sell, women, silly, laugh, men, lazy, people, complained, angry, carrying, riding, to please, bridge, frightened, kick, drowned.

Sentences:

A farmer and his son were taking their donkey to town to sell it.

The three of them were walking slowly and happily to town.

They passed some women in the road on their way to the town.

The women laughed to see such silly men walking when at least one of them could ride.

The farmer told his son to ride the donkey so the people might not laugh at them.

After awhile, they passed some men in the road.

"Look at that" one of the men said. "The lazy son wants to ride and make his poor old father walk."

The farmer quickly told his son to get off so he might ride instead.

Later, they passed a crowd of women and children walking in the road.

"What a mean father to ride and make his poor son walk when there is room for both."

The farmer pulled his son up behind him and they both rode the donkey so no one else would complain.

Then they passed a man and his wife who became very angry when they saw this.

"What cruel men you both are to ride such a small animal. You should carry him instead of trying to ride him."

The farmer wanted to please them so he and his son got off the donkey.

They tied the donkey to a pole and began to carry it across a bridge.

Many people came to laugh at such a funny looking group.

The donkey was frightened by the noise of the crowd and began to kick.

The donkey kicked so hard that he fell off of the bridge and was drowned.

Moral: When you try to please everyone, you usually wind up pleasing no one.

Questions:

Where were the farmer and his son taking their donkey?

Why did the women they met laugh at them?

Why were the men angry to see the son riding and the father walking?

Why were the next people angry to see the father riding and the son walking?

Why were both the man and wife angry to see the farmer and his son riding?

What did the farmer and his son do to please the man and wife?

Why did the crowd of people laugh at them?

What happened to the donkey?

What is the moral of the story?

ACTIVITY III THE DANCE

Material: Phonograph and popular records.

Procedure: The children are to select partners for the dance. They must carry on small talk conversations about any general topic such as dating, dancing, movies, etc. using a sotto voice. When the music stops they are to change partners and begin new conversations.

LESSON TWENTY

Arrange for parental permission to take the group to a restaurant for dinner. The parents may or may not accompany the group but since this is to be the final lesson for the intermediate group this would be an excellent time to discuss future plans for each of the children with their respective parents.

When the children have completed ordering their dinners and while you are all waiting for them to be served, read the fable of the Stork and the Fox. The parents are encouraged to join in since this will be an opportunity for them to better understand some of the problems their children have in communication.

When the meal is served, tell the children that they are free to converse but they must do so in a very soft voice.

THE STORK AND THE FOX

Cue words: embarrass, dinner, soup, shallow, flat, beak, chopped, dessert, melted, deep, course, get even.

The fox never liked the stork.

In fact, the fox would have eaten the stork but the stork had too many friends.

The fox always tried to embarrass the stork but the stork was a wise old bird.

One day, the fox held a dinner for some of the animals of the forest who like the stork.

Everyone was surprised because he invited the stork.

When everyone arrived, the fox announced that dinner was served.

The first course was soup which the fox served in a shallow soup dish.

The tiger and the rabbit, the lion and the mouse had no trouble at all.

The stork however had a long beak and could not get the soup out of the shallow dish.

The second course was meat that was chopped fine and served in a flat plate.

Again, the stork could not get the food out of the plate.

For dessert, the fox served ice cream in a flat dish and he brought the stork's last.

By that time it had melted and the stork had nothing to eat.

When it was time to leave, the stork thanked the fox for inviting him.

He did not seem angry at all.

In fact, he invited the fox to his house for dinner the following night.

When the fox sat down to eat he found a wonderful meal waiting for him.

But all the food was in deep dishes with narrow tops.

The fox could only smell the food while the stork ate.

Moral: Do unto others as you would have them do unto you.

Questions:

Why didn't the fox eat the stork?
Why had the fox invited the stork's friends?
How did the fox serve the soup?
How did he serve the rest of the meal?

Why did the stork have nothing to eat?
Did the stork show everyone he was angry?
What did he do when he left?
How did he get even with the fox?
What is the moral of the story?

APPENDIX

APPENDIX A

Test of Lip Reading Ability Using Homophonous Words

This test can be used prior to and after therapy to make a quantitative statement as the efficacy of the therapy employed. No normative data exists as yet on this particular test although a pilot study on twenty unsophisticated lip readers (normal hearing adults) elicited a mean of 64% with a standard deviation of 6.47%.

Homophenes:

mane, pane; main, mail; pail, bail, male; made, paid.

Method:

First write the cue words on the board (homophenes).

Give them with and without voice.

Give the sentences twice before allowing the class to write the sentences or say them aloud.

Scoring:

All homophonous words repeated correctly are valued at 2:5%.

All non-homophonous words are valued at 1.5%.

A score of 100% would be obtained by answering all sentences correctly.

Repeating the Test:

The same sentences are used for pre and post therapy testing but the order must be changed to prevent possible carry-over from the initial presentation.

Sentences are first presented in the order of the test and then in the following combinations:

Second presentation: 9,1,4,10,2,6,8,5,7,3.

Third presentation: 3,7,5,8,6,2,10,4,1,9.

Sentences:

1. The horse had a long mane.
2. The ball broke the glass pane.
3. There were trees on the main street.
4. Please mail this letter.
5. The pail was full of water.
6. They had to bail water from the boat.
7. He put the bait on the hook.
8. The puppy was a male.
9. Mother made chocolate cookies.
10. The girl paid a penny for the gum.

APPENDIX B

Topics for Additional Lip Reading Lessons

Things we can do.
Clothes we wear on different days.
Games we play in bad weather.
What can we see in the country?
What can we see in the city?
Where can we go?
Sounds we hear around us.
Objects found in the bedroom.
Objects found in the living room.
Objects found in the kitchen.
Objects found in the bathroom.
A sight seeing trip in Germany.
A sight seeing trip in Spain.
A sight seeing trip in Mexico.
A sight seeing trip around the world.
How do the Indians live?
How do the African natives live?
Different religions.
Customs across the world.
How much does it cost?